*I would like to thank everyone who helped me g*
*my son Charles for his good offices and every*
*for her patience in putting up with me day in*
*advice and that German know-how of hers. Th*
*supplying the necessary raw materials. So to*
*little, I thank you all once more.*

CONTENTS

# Chapter One

*Our Daily Bread*

Thick dark brown hair parted neatly on the left-hand side was held firmly in place with liberal dollops of *Brylcream*. The snag was you dared not let anyone pat you on the head too hard otherwise the stuff could come pouring out of your ears. Not that anyone was likely to pat you on the head in those immediate post-war days. A bloke had to make his own luck then. Survival would be the name of the game.

Solid honest to goodness shoulders and broad with it tested to the full the seams of the brand new sports jacket I was wearing courtesy of His Majesty's Service. Gleaming white teeth bore testimony and more than compensated for the twenty or so army fillings that had gone into making them so. Although I did have to admit that at times I felt my mouth was just one great chasm of bone and putty pulsating, even hardening, all the time especially when I tried to laugh. Straight-faced therefore would have to be the order of the day as far as any future job interviews were concerned. But for all that, and I make no apologies for this self appraisal, I just had to concede that I liked that look of the newly demobbed soldier who beamed out at me from that Demob Tailor's shop window.

It was round about that time too that I remembered going right off Allan Ladd after reading how they had to make him look taller by means of specially made built-in high heeled shoes. I swore that there would be none of that rubbish for me. I prided myself that I stood five feet four and a half in my JohnL's, without any gimmickry whatsoever. I was all me. I even remember the Demob Tailor saying to me that great day. "You're a man all the way down to your ankles, sir."

Then for some reason known only to himself he proceeded ruthlessly to scissor off four or five inches of perfectly good cloth from my trouser legs so that I could walk unfettered. I felt then that it was a scandalous waste of perfectly good material and told him so. But deep down within myself I had to admit they fitted a treat after that.

I just felt that life had to be good for the emerging victors at that time. I had done my whack, there was no disputing that. You didn't need a chest full of medals to prove anything. Medals never did interest me. The main thing was my health was improving by the day, my head too and my confidence with it. War stories were all the go in the pubs when I got back. And fiction was rampant. Fact was relegated to second place. That didn't worry me either. For improvisation if needed had always been one of my own strong points. I could embellish even the truth with the best of them. Suffice to say I had a kitbag full of duty-free fags and three weeks of my demob leave still to run and a wealth of stories still to tell. Some true and some that could even match the best fiction of the day . . .

But one had to tread warily in those Glasgow pubs shortly after the war. Not being one of the first out made the going all the more difficult as time began to wear on in the literal sense. Competition was becoming fierce when I arrived on the scene. I mean it wasn't good enough to just say that you alone had machine-gunned a few of the enemy. The mere fact that I'd actually been there was immaterial. I was still outnumbered by the fiction writers.

"Stories" had to have that little bit extra to help satisfy those sometimes-insatiable demands. You had to come up with something really spectacular before your audience would deem it worthy of a drink. Everyone was getting in on the act. Postmen. Lamplighters. Even school janitors. Anyone in fact who could honestly say that they had legitimately worn a uniform during the war. Not to mention all those war movies John Wayne was making at the time. All those things had to be contended with. So I saw no reason why I shouldn't join the fiction merchants and make a few bob too. No one else was doing me any favours. The army may have downgraded me as far as my health was concerned. But they had diminished nothing else . . . My brain-box may now be a little more dented than it was before. But the war was over and I was alive.

So why shouldn't I cash in too? And this I did. I decided to settle for the slightly hesitant approach. "As far as I'm concerned anyone could have done what I did. I just happened to be in the right place at the right time. It was either them or me." That they liked. To be perfectly honest that they loved. Drinks began to flow my way for a change. But care was needed. Especially when you'd had a few drinks down you at the time for timing had to be right. A good idea was to make a quick exit as soon as possible before the facts could be checked out. I was learning fast. I had to. The competition was becoming even fiercer.

Despite all the stories of war and danger experienced by the storyteller money just seemed to drain away as I found out to my dismay. So I decided to dispense with the frivolous and concentrate more on my future. Because no one was going to do it for me that's for sure. Nor did I intend to go remotely near any mental hospital as was suggested by some.

So with this particular thought in mind I dropped by my local Labour Exchange for a quiet look round. The place was deserted. It was as though the entire East End of Glasgow was either dead or fully employed. Large posters adorned the walls. "Look ahead." "It's Over And Done With But You're Not!"

"Sign On For Work Now . . . " "Don't Delay . . . Do It Today!" It was compelling stuff. I turned to go.

"Looking for a job chum?" I looked round. A tall thin bespectacled youth with "Reserved Occupation" written all over his visage was eyeing me quizzically from behind the "Vacancies" Section. I blew a mouthful of duty-free cigarette smoke his way momentarily clouding his vision. Inexcusable my action may well have been but it was the way I was at that moment. And anyway I felt I was entitled to my manic moments just like anyone else. "Who me . . . ?.No, No . . . I was just passing," I replied. "Just thought I'd come in and have a look round. Anyway I've got plenty of time yet. I'm still on demob leave, you know." He took out a handkerchief and began cleaning his glasses then began to flick over some files that were lying on the desk in front of him. "That's where you're going wrong, mate." He smiled knowledgeably. "You don't need to wait till your demob leave's finished you know. That's where you blokes lose out . . . " He must have noticed my eyes lighting up or something at his words for he immediately went into some sort of recruiting drive. "Grab one of these jobs while you're still on leave and believe you me there's some stoaters here. It's two lots of wages you know; that's the way to look at it. It's double your money. And that can't be bad. Just think of it . . . !"

I already was thinking of it and began straight away to tot it all up in my head. It certainly warranted attention. I had to face facts. My gratuity was ebbing away fast and despite all my ingenuity, I was slowly but surely running out of war stories. A soldier on demob leave was only as good as his improvisations in those days. And I was fast running out of tales of gallantry true and untrue . . . I was already beginning to find out that the truer your story was the less they wanted to believe you.

"What have you got?" I struggled to try and strike just the right balance between keenness and a nonchalance I didn't really have. The clerk looked up from his file. "What did you do before the war?" That was a hard one. And it threw me momentarily. Just what had I done before the war? For a moment I just couldn't think. Nothing was coming through to me. The only thing I could remember doing before the war was forging my mother's Co-operative cheques which that great institution issued to customers for every purchase they made. And being the youngest of the family I always got the job of going to the Co-op for their special sausages in those days.

Even at the tender age of fourteen and having just left school I got it from a very enlightened source that the Co-op's sausages although listed at fourpence, sixpence, and eightpence per pound were all of the very same quality.

An apprentice butcher who had worked in that same shop had leaked this information to me free gratis and for nothing. It meant in fact and this was invaluable info believe you me, that even if those sausages were four, six or even eight pence per pound they were still the very same sausages. The variance in prices was just a trick of the trade my source informed me.

"Get me two pounds of sixpenny sliced sausages" my mother would tell me. A middle of the road woman was my mother. She could never afford the best. But she would never ever buy the cheapest. "And don't forget to get your dividend chit." Needless to say I never ever forgot. But I never ever got the sixpence a pound sausages either. I got the fourpence a pound stuff then proceeded to alter the price on the chit to read a shilling when in fact it had only cost eightpence. Thus making me a net profit of four whole pence. So what in fact was I to tell the clerk what I was before the war. That . . . I was a . . . very bad forger ?

The Labour Exchange clerk obviously didn't think my reply would be all that important. He pointed to a sheaf of papers in front of him. "Here's one that might suit you." he said. "despatch clerk wanted for large bakery in the East End." I hesitated. "Would there be any touch-typing involved?" I asked. "For I can do that. I was on a course for that in the army." He shook his head. "I don't know. I don't think so. What is touch-typing anyway?" I hesitated once more. Then he pounced. "Just think about it," he smiled. "Two lots of wages for almost four weeks; plus your demob pay. Not to be sneezed at." He waved the sheets of paper in front of me tantalizingly.

"What's the greengages like?" I countered. He then leaned over, looked furtively to his left and to his right and whispered in my ear. "Seven and a half quid a week and as many pan loaves as you can carry away with you." I demurred. "Oh and it says here they're thinking of opening a canteen." Bully for them I thought. "Bu-But I've never done anything like that before" I stammered. "I've got no previous experience." "It doesn't matter a bugger." he hissed. "They probably won't ask you anyway. They're desperate for men." So were The Foreign Legion I remembered thinking and was about to say so. But the interview was terminated as far as he was concerned. "Here's your Green Card. Hand it in as soon as you get to the bakery. Be there at one o'clock tomorrow."

I mulled it over in bed that night and decided to give it a whirl before dozing off. And that very next morning all spruced up I presented myself at that large somewhat unappealing bakery gate. "despatch clerk." It had a ring to it. Probably a collar and tie job I concluded. Couldn't be anything else. The very designation said it all. I'd be able to try out my newly acquired prowess as a touch-typist at a later date. There was no rush.

A cool afternoon breeze played on my face as I handed in my Green Card to the gateman. "Just hold on there, sir and I'll get someone to attend to you straight away." It was good to know that the old courtesies were still around. Old fashioned maybe. But it may well be that my military bearing had prompted the attention being so readily afforded me. I was glad I had come. My misgivings were disappearing quicker than a rat down a drainpipe. There were many things in the bakery's favour. It was handy. Ten minutes walk away and best of all no bus fares. Money for old boots was a phrase that readily sprang to mind. "Someone will attend to you very shortly, sir." I nodded my head in thanks to the gateman. Politeness cost nothing my mother had always told me. Just as well for I was on my uppers.

"Sir ?" I blinked away that April sun from my eyes to observe a tall white-coated man in his late forties. He was eyeing me up up from head to toe. "You'll be the young man from the Labour Exchange no doubt. Just follow me please!" He then led me away from that delightful sunlight and along a dark passageway to what I could only presume was the Bakery proper. It was really dark. The only light to be seen was a trickle from a skylight window high up on the roof. Mr Whitecoat strode on regardless and I tried to keep up with his brisk pace. Suddenly he began to throw his arms about in an effort to put me in the picture. The deeper in we got the warmer it got. And the din began to get deafening. "There you have it, sir. This is the layout. This is where it all happens. All we ask is that you give the job a fair trial. I know only too well that it can't be easy for you young ex-service men to try to come to terms with work after all the excitement of war. But you must know yourself that you've got to start somewhere and it might as well be here!"

I didn't want to fall out with him there and then so I just kept following on. Then bedlam reached an all time high. Three tiered trolleys laden with little white loaves were being hurtled all around me. I counted at least twenty. The trolleys were out-numbered only by the piles of loaves, which were heaped unceremoniously on top of them. Not only were there loaves there. There were men there too, little white men who looked as though they had lived all of their little white lives in little white houses. And these little men shoved, propelled and pushed those mobile trolleys full of loaves and somehow miraculously managed to get them all into some sort of alignment ready for despatch.

At least I gathered that was the reason for the exercise. Suddenly, the designation "Despatch Clerk" was beginning to assume sinister connotations in my head. Not only that but it was becoming decidedly warmer too. Not that Mr. Whitecoat was bothered one whit. Not him. Dodging laden trolleys was a hobby he had obviously perfected. And no doubt hoped every one else had too as he rabbitted on to himself about Scotland's place in post-war Britain gesticulating as he went.

But that was the least of my troubles as I recalled then. It had become so warm that my brand new demob sports jacket was beginning to weigh very heavily on my shoulders. And the liberal dollops of *Brylcream* which I lavishly indulged in for special occasions were beginning to pour unashamedly down the back of my neck. I remember making my mind up fast as I dodged another trolley. I was not prepared to like this job . . .

That gatehouse and fresh cool air seemed a million miles away. The soldier in me sought an escape route. I had almost found one when Mr You-Know-Who stopped in front of what could only be described as a small conveyor belt measuring about six feet across. Roller belts thereon were coming up through the floor in a steady seemingly unending movement. They then rose upwards right on through the ceiling thus completing a continuous circle. I had never ever seen anything like it in all my life.

Needless to say the roller belts were filled from end to end with small steaming oblong newly baked loaves. The rows of loaves on each tray appeared to be coming out of some subterranean oven freshly baked all ready to be plucked out before the trays were then merrily sent back up through the ceiling to be filled yet again with more raw dough. A complete revolution in more ways than one I thought.

A little bloke smaller than myself (I immediately loved him for that alone) stood in front of this ingenious piece of machinery He was stripped to the waist. Quite oblivious of me or Mr Whitecoat and with great dexterity he kept plucking these loaves out from their trays with the thumb and forefinger of each hand. He kept working his way inwards until the trays were empty. It was a simultaneous movement bordering on the miraculous. He plucked those red-hot oblongs from each end still working inwardly all the time. He would then place the loaves neatly on the trolley behind him until it was full. Whereupon it was hurtled away. But there was an element of danger there too I thought. Because if those trays were not emptied in time and those brown loaves, precious though they may be, were not extricated expeditiously they could soon be above you out of reach and through that roof again to heaven knows where. And a fresh laden tray would be arriving up chest high demanding your immediate attention. The motion was unending. But he never missed a trick or a loaf come to that did our little performer all the time Mr Whitecoat and I were stood there. He made it look all so easy. Monotonous, but easy.

Then dramatically this human loaf extricator extraordinaire, suddenly realised he had an audience and took time off from emptying those trays to shake me firmly and flourly by the hand. Then without missing as much as one loaf he turned back immediately again to his little revolving trays as though he had never been away.

Introduction over, Mr Whitecoat began gesticulating even more than ever trying to point out the intricacies of the modern bakery. "Up there" he bawled trying to make himself heard above the noise that was erupting all around. He pointed to the ceiling once more. "Up there," he repeated, "the bakers stick the raw un-baked loaves into the trays in batches of six." He looked down at me. "Are you with me ? "I *was* actually. But only because I hadn't yet figured out an escape route!

He then made a circular movement with both hands and cupped his hands to his mouth and roared. "The loaves then travel upwards, then along, then down into the ovens. When baked to perfection they descend here under us and then up to where we are here for Albert to extract and place on these trolleys provided. And believe you me those loaves are baked all right. They're baked to perfection when they leave those ovens !" I didn't doubt him for a moment but refrained from saying so.

I tried to let my heart go out to those brave bakers whoever and whatever they may be. I really did try to feel for them as did Mr You Know Who. Churlish it may well have been of me but I had already made my mind up. He could stuff his job. And I tried to tell him so but he wasn't listening. He was still extolling the virtues and the dedication of those bakers. "I don't want the fucking job." I shouted "I'm just not fucking interested! "

But he rambled on and on. "There's nothing to it. All you have to do is what Albert is doing right now. That is, pick up the loaves gently with the thumb and forefinger of each hand remembering to work inwards till the tray is empty then you're ready for the next tray. And always ensure that your loaves are placed neatly on the trolley behind you ready to be wheeled away by the wheelers. So on and so on . . . You'll soon get the hang of it! "I tried one last despairing attempt. "I don't want the bloody job. It's not for me. I'm not well enough trained." "Nonsense" he countered. "You'll pick it up in no time."

He then grabbed my arm and led me over to yet another never ending ever-revolving tray and an ever present and ever efficient little Albert. He then made a perfunctory introduction with his hands. "Albert; this is Eddie, your relief plucker . . . Eddie, this is Albert. Eddie . . . Albert . . . Albert Eddie. He'll be your relief for the next half hour ! "And with that Mr Whitecoat stomped off still waving his arms in the air.

Albert was already peeling off the little red rubber tips that were supposed to prevent the fingers from becoming burned. That is should your thumb and forefinger inadvertently pierce a loaf midst plucking. He beamed at me as he handed them over. "Mind and keep these protectors on" he counselled not unkindly. Then just before shuffling off he turned. "By the way I've left you half a loaf and some scrape. And if I was you I'd get that jaiket aff sharpish." And with those invaluable tips still ringing in my ears he too was gone. Suddenly I felt very alone. Very, very alone indeed!

What to do now ? That indeed was the question. Those loaves were awaiting my immediate attention that's what. In fact those loaves already were heading for the ceiling. I tried desperately to remember the drill; pluck, turn, and place. So I did just that by reaching up and plucking two loaves from that disappearing tray. But for all that I knew deep down that I wasn't doing it fast enough. I tried. God knows I tried but it just wasn't working. The steaming oblong monstrosities were rising above my head irrevocably and disappearing heavenwards through the ceiling. I tried to up the tempo and succeeded modestly. But then again five out of six wasn't too bad I reckoned. But it was the plucking then the turning so as to place them neatly on the trolley behind that was slowing me down. And try as I might I just couldn't match that co-ordination of little Albert's pluck, turn, and place. That was it, wasn't it. Or was it pluck, place, and turn?

Despair was beginning to envelop me. I made a decision, a reckless one some may say. But I made it. I decided to scrap the lift, turn and place routine in favour of a lift, turn, and lob system hoping against hope to step up on my performance by lobbing the loaves over my shoulder and praying that they landed the right way up on the trolley. But alas they never did. It was then that I knew I was losing the battle of the loaves.

My thumbs and forefingers were red raw by this time. And ironically they were almost indistinguishable in colour from those very same little gadgets that were provided to protect me from that very torture. "Help! Help!" I shouted, with all the strength I could muster But it was to no avail. Help would never be mine. Of that I was most certain . . . Dodging eighty-eight's, mortar bombs and snipers was one thing. Dodging red hot loaves was another. So I decided there and then to desert!

"What the hell do you think you're playing at, matey?" I turned trying to tease some dough from my hair at the same time. A big burly bloke with an off-white jacket and apron and a ridiculous looking hat was standing there hands on hips looking down at me scathingly. I tried to match his stare. "What do you mean?"

I shouted back at him. "What am *I* doing? I'm only trying to prise these bloody loaves off the trays so that you can put some fresh ones in. That's what I'm doing!" "You mean that's what you're supposed to be doing. But you're not bloody well doing it, are you?" It was then that a thought struck me. This must be HIM. The Baker from Above! This indeed must be He. The Anti-Christ! I came right back at him. "I'm doing the best I can!"

He leaned over. I could taste the dough on his breath. "Well, matey" He said. "I'm here to tell you you're bloody best isn't good enough so it's not. There's me sticking the loaves in the ovens up there to be passed along the belt for baking. To be then taken off by you after they're baked, then on to the trolleys for despatch. And what are you doing? You're only despatching them back up to me again. What am I supposed to do with them? Bake the fucking things again?"

I was taking no more from him and lunged forward but I unfortunately tripped on some down-trodden loaves that were lying on the floor. I struggled to my feet only to be grabbed by Mr Whitecoat and held back. He then took up position between me and the big baker. Albert was there too, back and duly refreshed. No doubt poised ready to pounce once more on those trays. Mr Whitecoat squeezed my arm firmly. "Steady now. Steady!" He then took command and ordered the big baker away.

Give Mr Whitecoat his due. He did apologise to me for him and Albert being late back. Seemingly there had been a breakdown at another rotating oven which had warranted his attention. "You know it's a damned nuisance when ovens stop like that." "It's a fucking pity this one didn't stop" I sobbed spreading my hands out to let him see the damage him and his loaves had done to to my fingers. "Dear dear" he said examining them minutely. " I'll go and get the First Aid Box right away. Not to worry. Just teething troubles . . . " I couldn't find an answer to that one. And could only watch and wonder numbly as little Albert plucked turned and placed those little loaves ever so neatly on the trolley behind him. He still managed to make it all look so easy . . .

Mr Whitecoat went on and on whilst he dressed my molten fingers. "It's like I was saying, Mr . . . Mr . . . " I withdrew my fingers. He had forgotten my name. The bastard had forgotten my name already. Yet he still went on. "Like I was saying, sir. Just give the job a chance. You'll make an ideal relief for Albert. You'll get to know one another and will get on fine. The job will grow on you." How prophetic he was he'll never know. For it already was growing on me. Flour was beginning to sprout out of my ears. "And of course, getting a Works

Canteen will be a tremendous boost to us. And would you believe it. They're actually toying with the idea of getting music played while you work. Whatever will they think of next! "

It may well have been the birth of "Music While You Work" round about that time for all I knew. But I wasn't listening any more. My brand new sports jacket which I'd had no time to remove during the plucking process felt as though it had been ironed on with me still in it and it was beginning to hurt something awful. So I seized the moment. A stroke of God's own sunlight filtering below a doorway not all that far away from where I was standing seemed to beckon me. So I started running . . . And running . . . And running . . . !

I expected the worse when I reported back to the Labour Exchange a day or so later and I wasn't disappointed. I was immediately told to report to the supervisor who laid it on the line to me even before I'd sat down. "Your payment benefit will cease forthwith for a period of six weeks." "Why?" I asked not impertinently. "Because," he said, "you turned down a perfectly good job without a valid reason; that's why. It's standard procedure. Do you understand your position?" I nodded, and got up to go in case he would offer me another "position". As I made for the door he called out. "If you're in financial difficulties due to this decision you're perfectly entitled to apply for National Assistance . . . "

I breathed a sigh of relief the moment I was on the other side of that door. The loss of benefit was a blow. Of course it was. There was no denying that. But at least I now had the full use of my fingers and thumbs again. However there was no escaping the fact that my financial crisis couldn't have struck at a worse possible time.

For that very morning I had received wonderful news. News which I had been waiting for for some considerable time. There was very little time to waste. For I had a mission to perform. A very special mission. And that mission was to get a certain V.I.P out of Nazi Germany. Quickly. Very quickly!

# Chapter Two

*Fighting the Good Fight*

. . . It may well have been borne out of sheer selfishness, even fear, but I blamed the powers-that-be for all that was about to befall us that awful night; they and their overwhelming desire to intensify the race for the Rhine. The retreating German army were being irritatingly obdurate as far as the Allies were concerned and had dug themselves determinedly in and were occupying a strategic point in and around a railway line on the outskirts of Overloon. And according to what we were told it would take one almighty battle to move them on.

For once our Top Brass were to be proved right. Overloon, not being one of the better known towns in Holland would soon turn out to be one of the most bitter and bloody battles of the war. While it was true to say that there had been much blood spilled before especially in and around Caen in Normandy, the fields of Overloon would turn out to be the daddy of them all. And I can say with hand on heart and without any bombast whatsoever that anyone who survived that awful dark October night would agree with me to this day.

Not only were the Germans entrenched behind a long line of rail track but they also had snipers installed in a large signal box with a commanding overall view to kill. All this despite an over optimistic quote from our Intelligence people that enemy morale was at an all time low. Pity they hadn't asked us about ours. It was hardly party time where we were either because the Germans were more than matching our fire with a sustained and frightening ferocity.

Despite all this we were ordered forward. The main advance on the river Rhine had to proceed. It must not be halted at any cost. The command was given and we mere soldiers would obey that command, get riddled with bullets and be bloody proud, nay privileged so to do. And so with the Vickers 303 machine gun specially mounted for effect on our Bren carrier we inched forward through torrential rain on that horrid night.

Infantry flanked us on either side with Sherman tanks to our rear. My particular task as spelled out to me by my Section Commander Alex Price was to get an inch perfect reading if possible on my Barr & Stroud Rangefinder to enable the gunners to traverse that signal box and silence it. That was the theory. The practical aspect was somewhat different. Visibility was getting less and less by the minute but our somewhat tentative advance had to continue. There was all that "Pride and Privilege" stuff to think of . . .

An enemy flare lit up the dark turbulent sky highlighting us and giving those snipers their first good look at us as a target. They must have liked what they saw, as did their machine-gunners, for the rat-a-tat of their guns filled the dark night air. We leapt off-truck as we were trained to do and lay spread-eagled beside our vehicles trying to bury our heads and as much of our bodies as we could in the muck and slime of that field till the onslaught abated. Then it was on-truck and forward again. It was the only way to do it or it could be all over for you. It was a drill movement. But it was a good drill movement. It kept you alive!

We had also been drilled to take note of the tail end of every flare. "Do not move till the flare dies in the sky," was the message, so we did just that and forward we moved in the murkiness and the darkness. And the target? One solitary signal box. Bogged down by the mud our advance was painfully slow but despite rain careering down our faces and into our eyes progress was achieved and we were now almost beginning to see the full picture. So it was onwards and onwards and onwards. Then came another bombardment of eighty-eights and mortar bombs. So it was head and face down again but just for seconds this time. For we were almost within firing range of that signal box and I was just about to give our gunners a reading on it when disaster struck. The gun mounting specially adapted to support the weight of the Vickers and hold it in position suddenly withdrew her support and collapsed on us thus rendering the achievable unachievable.

Our Vickers was now useless. There we were on top of the enemy so far advanced we could almost see them. Could almost smell them. Somehow we had got there. But tragically we were unable to return their fire now that we'd got there. And all hell was now raining on us from those enemy entrenchments we had squelched through shell holes to get to. But the manual of war didn't quite cover such exigencies like collapsible bloody machine gun mountings. Did it?

Heavy rain was still coursing down on our panic stricken faces as we strove as best we could to right that sudden mounting collapse despite the cramped conditions inside our carrier. Soaking wet hands, hindered even more by leaking oil from gun parts, grappled in the dark to get that mounting righted and our gun firing again. But it wasn't working. Nothing was working. They were gunning us from all angles now. We were wide open. Take your bloody pick Fritz!

"Hold the tripod arm up a bit." Price was shouting frenziedly as Sonny and I wrestled with that mounting from our crouching positions. "It's not easy you know." I roared back at him at the same time trying to coax some heat into my now numb right hand, by blowing into it.

"Christ Almighty, nothing's fucking easy!" he roared back like a man demented. Smithy had now clambered back from the driving seat in an effort to help us get things right, but it was no use. We were only making enemies of ourselves by getting in each other's way. Small arms fire was now ricocheting the sides of our carrier. Although none of us said it we all knew that rifle fire would be useless against this heavy onslaught on us by the Germans. And our infantrymen were too far back to assist. It was just one more example of an exercise that wasn't in the drill book.

Only by clenching my teeth could I refrain from crying out loudly and angrily in the night. I could have taken my chances and jumped out and ran. But I was damned if I was going to let them all see that I couldn't take it so I lent a hand again to Price, Smithy and Sonny to try and remedy the fault in the mounting, but it was to be a lost cause. In daylight it may have been just possible. But in pitch darkness it was just going to be impossible . . .

Then suddenly British and German artilleries went into full blast. One great crescendo of noise and flashes and the whole night sky was being lit up. It was ear-bursting stuff from both sides. It sounded as though both artilleries had suddenly decided to empty their arsenals of bombs and to hell with it all. But our big stuff appeared to be coming off best. And so there we were, a Bren carrier, a Vickers with a defective mounting and a crew arguing with each other, positioned well forward, but unable to play any part in the proceedings other than watch and hope.

Our infantry was still doing their bit too, advancing steadily, gaining ground more quickly despite the mire and the bedlam. They must have been well aware of our circumstances for we had been shouting long and hard enough. The panic within us had not subsided one bit. Anger and frustration set in amongst us aboard our beleaguered carrier, stopping just short of fist-fighting with each other.

Not only were our infantry doing their stuff but our artillery were now getting to grips with it all and beginning to plaster that railway line. Our division was hitting back and no mistake.. And we were winning. Everyone was winning. Everyone except the four of us in that carrier that is . . .

That fact was borne out as slobbering hysterical Germans flashed past our carrier their manic shouts of surrender filling the night air with grotesque looking strips of green camouflage material still clinging to their helmets. Some had hands on their heads. Some with hands in the air. It appeared to be all too much for them too for they kept running and running . . . But they were running in the right direction. It was over for them. All they would have to do would be to suffer the indignity and the boredom of a POW camp somewhere well away from it all.

But there was to be no such luck for us. We were stuck there as targets, more or less where we were . . . !

With both hands clasped firmly to my ears to try and blot it all out I was again within an ace of joining them. Nor was I alone with my thoughts methinks as we stared at each other in the gloom and at that bloody gun-mounting that had just gone and collapsed on us. German machine gun fire was still strafing staccato style against the sides of our stationery carrier as we crouched inside for cover.

If it did nothing else that ominous rat-a-tat was telling us to do something quickly or they would do it for us. Then I surprised everyone even myself. I decided that the only way we were going to save ourselves and get out of the mess we were in was for someone to lie across the carrier and to try and hold that mounting by hand. Then to hold it firmly enough to enable our machine gun to fire. Easier said than done. But it was one option. And at that moment we didn't have any. Nor was it just because it was my suggestion. I most certainly didn't want to be put to death. But being executed sitting down I wanted even less.

It may well be that I was the obvious choice to do this since I was no gunner but merely a rangetaker. And as it was pointless me taking readings when we had nothing to attack anyone with when we'd got it. Somehow it just made sense. So despite that old army maxim about not volunteering for anything I decided that for once I would be the exception that proved the rule.

Frightened to death little old me would have my death-wish granted as it were and I would lie across the top of the carrier and try to hold the mounting steady. It would mean alas my exposing myself even more to the enemy than was necessary. To be brutally frank I would be exposing myself from the neck up and was all those snipers in that signal box needed. But I felt within myself that I wanted out away from it all one way or another before I went stark raving mad!

"Are you sure you want to do this?" shouted Pricey trying to make himself heard. I nodded. " Over. " "No, I roared, but I'm going to fucking do it anyway." And to be truthful I was fast running out of prayers and wanted the whole thing over and done with. It was either that or running. I hoped he wouldn't see the terror in my face in the darkness. I then lay on my back with knees bent. Pricey placed the gun back on the tripod whilst I strove to hold the wonky leg up to secure alignment with the other two thus allowing the gun to fire. The weight of the leg and the gun was heavier than I thought but somehow I managed to keep it steady. If that didn't work, nothing would.

But it did work. Miraculously it did work. After a couple of failed attempts what I hoped would happen did happen, I tried an extra heave upwards. Pricey tried the gun handles once more. And the gun fired. "Keep it that way, Mac." he roared triumphantly in the dark then proceeded to traverse that railway line with 303's just as we'd intended to do before. More traversing fire by Pricey on the railway line then he tapped into a traverse of that signal box!

And all the while I was holding on to that tripod leg for my very life trying to keep it steady and ad-libbing prayers at the same time. Empty 303 casings were whizzing past me at 500 rounds a minute as I lay there on my back. The old Vickers was doing her stuff now alright. It was all very heartening but I felt my arms were reaching near breaking point. I began to wish it was all over. I wasn't going to be able to take much more and tried to withdraw as much as I dared under the side of the carrier to protect myself just a little more from enemy fire without at the same time compromising the concentration of our gunners. Then significantly that signal box fell silent. I began to wonder at all those purple colours that were surrounding us all of a sudden. And those flashes of light! Was it some sort of freak lightning that was exploding all around..? Smoke . . . People whispering . . . People shouting . . . Noises! Noises! . . .

I was lying on my back on the ground. Yet I felt I was not on the ground. Could have been a board of some sort. Above me was an expanse of white canvas. What was it? Khaki-clad figures were moving all around me. But there was no one I knew. No familiar faces. There were other figures lying on the ground too. But they weren't near enough me to ask them who they were or even who I was, or where we were. Plenty of soldiers with white bands on their arms were scurrying about all around lifting bundles and putting them down on the ground with the others . . .

Lots of noise too and the thunder of guns and of explosions somewhere near. No one to ask. No one to speak to. No one to confide in, but no one. Some of those figures were lying very still. I wouldn't ask those who were very still. They wouldn't know. I would ask some of the ones who moved and who were also on the ground lying on boards like I was . . .

Then they told me. I didn't ask but they told me. They told me where I was. I was in an R.A.P. tent with lots of other people. "What was an R.A.P.?" I asked them. A Regimental Aid Post was indeed a tent being used as a temporary hospital near the Front to help people get better who had been wounded in action they told me. But those people who weren't moving as they lay on those boards on the ground nearby me wouldn't get better would they . . . ? I asked. But they wouldn't tell me . . .

Then they gave me something to drink and I felt a little better. What they gave me to drink was very sweet and I liked it. I asked one of the soldiers who had a white band round his arm what time it was, but he didn't say. He did tell me however that I would be moving soon to where it would be a lot quieter. I was glad to hear that because the noise was becoming unbearable. Pandemonium in fact would be a better word for it all. I tried to raise my head but had to let it fall back again. It had become one great whirling pool over which I had no control. I wanted to be sick. And I *was* sick, very sick. I tried to close my eyes and I wished I were dead. Maybe I already was. And the feeling wasn't pleasant. I just wanted it all to go away. No one came near me. No one was telling me anything. I just lay there and watched again as those soldiers with the white arm bands came and went carrying people on stretchers in and out of that tent flap. But I could still hear familiar rumbles not all that far away.

I tried to sum up enough energy to ask one of the soldiers where I was and what they were going to do with me. One of them whispered to me that he was an orderly and his job was to look after me till I got better. They then lifted me from the ground on to a stretcher and carried me outside and placed me in the back of a truck. It was all very hazy. And my head was still buzzing from it all whatever it was that had happened to me. The back of the truck was sparsely lit but I could discern another couple of stretchers in there with me. At least I was not alone. Instructions were being issued outside. I could hear shouts, then the truck revved up and soon it began swaying from side to side. We were on the move. The noises of guns and shells were getting fainter and fainter and I was glad. Perhaps I wasn't supposed to be but I was. There were many bumps on that road. The driver was making a lot of swerving movements with his vehicle and I was sick again. My head was not telling me as much as before and I heard no more sounds. But I was beginning to feel a little better.

When I awoke I knew instinctively that I was somewhere far away. And why did I in my confused state know that? Because I could hear birds singing outside wherever it was they had taken me and because from where I'd just come from no birds sang. They dared not. Otherwise they too would have been blown to smithereens!

I tried my best to try and take it all in. But my head still wasn't helping me in my effort to piece things together. The curious thing was that despite a constant thumping around my brain I could feel no pain. My mouth didn't appear to be capable of producing enough saliva but that was about all. Everything else was bearable especially after I managed to turn my head and have a look around me. There was an uncanny stillness about the place. Maybe it wasn't a hospital at all. If not, what was it. And where was it . . . ?

Perhaps it was a mobile guard-room. But then again, there were no guards, nor any Redcaps. I wasn't violent. So they wouldn't need any of these people. I wouldn't hurt a soul. You could ask anyone. I clenched my fists. I had two hands. I stretched out. Two arms, all there. I ran my hands down my thighs. I was bodily intact. Everything was in it's proper place. I could even wiggle my toes. Why then was I here? There was no blood either. An orderly came over. "Where am I? Please tell me." I begged. He smiled down at me. "You're about twelve kilometres down the line. I can't tell you any more. Don't worry. You're not going back there!" I believed him. Why shouldn't I believe him? Why should he lie to me? He had no reason to!

It was coming back. My head was beginning to tell me things once more, mixed-up stuff maybe at first. But it was slowly coming back to me. I closed my eyes and tried a question and answer exercise to try and sort out my befuddled brain. What was that Number One Gunner's name again? Alex something or other, Yes, Alex, Alex Price from Manchester. That's what it was. He was with me when we were transferred from the Argylls to the Royal Northumberland Fusiliers.

Yes. We were the only Vickers Machine Gun Unit in the army. Our weapon was unique. A relic from the Great War it was. That's right Alex was his name. A great Manchester City fan if I remembered correctly. And I was remembering . . . And that was good. My head must be getting better. Then that Number Two Gunner. What was his name. I didn't know him, a last minute replacement or something. I didn't want to remember any more. I was so tired . . .

Now it was all coming back to me. We were unique in more ways than one. We were all ex-Argylls myself included, for although we were officially members of the Royal Northumberland Fusiliers, we were allowed to still wear the badge of the Argyll and Sutherland Highlanders. So we were half-Jock and half-Geordie I suppose. And what of Smithy? He owed me three bob. Never paid me back yet. He was our driver? My best mate too. We'd all been together since D plus one . . . I could remember them all now. Yes they'd made Alex Price or Pricey up to Section Commander no less . . . Deserved it but . . . He was good at his job . . . I felt I didn't want to sleep any more . . . Even though I felt very weak. Maybe they didn't like you sleeping too much. Bad for morale and all that sort of stuff I suppose . . .

An orderly came over, lit a cigarette and bent over me. "Sorry I can't give you one mate. Not allowed to in case you've got to get a jag and might make you sick." He pointed over his shoulder and smiled. "I'll bet you're glad you're out of that lot, eh?" I didn't argue with him. I didn't fight with him either. I checked myself once more for arms and legs for he was giving me some queer looks that orderly was despite all his smiles. But everything seemed to be in it's proper place!

But why then had they taken me to this place? Had I ran away from my mates? Was I some sort of coward . . . ? Had I assaulted an officer? Was I going on some sort of compassionate leave? Something was wrong and that worried me. There were more shouts from inside and outside the tent, then it was on-truck time again. Down more bumpy roads for what I reckoned to be about ten kilometres. I knew because I was counting in my head. We were then taken off the truck to be carried yet again inside a very large building and along a very long corridor, which felt every bit as long as the journey we had covered in the truck. I eased myself up from my stretcher to see we were now inside a very large hall. It could have been some sort of assembly hall, I thought. I felt a lot better. At times my head was still sore and I couldn't see properly at times. But I was paying attention. The moment we were all placed on stretchers, which were still on the floor, we were informed that this was to be our place of residence for the time being. I was to find out later that it was a part of a monastery that had been commandeered by the army to be used as a hospital. This one time place of worship would now be a place purely for the sick, the wounded, the dying, and the dead. It was all very eerie.

I lay back and wondered. Where were they taking me? I had been told nothing. It may be that my head was not quite right at that moment but I had a right to know. I had a brain inside this head of mine regardless what anyone may think to the contrary. I most certainly was not stupid. Off my head a little maybe. But stupid, never. My eyes could see all sorts of wounded people around me. There were some bodies there with no legs at all. I could tell this by the lengths of the folds in the blankets that covered them. I could even tell if they had no arms or only one arm as I lay there. I began to get good at it. The give-away was the varying lengths of the covering blanket. The mere fact that there were so many different types of wounded and even walking-wounded there not to mention the dying should have told me something. But I think I was beginning to figure it all out.

This wasn't just a temporary hospital. It was a clearing house for the dead and wounded. The hospital people just didn't have time to segregate the various types of wounded that were there. My observations were being proved right. Orderlies began to set up beds; real beds in that massive hall. Blankets and linen were being brought in by orderlies and nurses and piled high all ready to adorn those beds. But they were also wheeling out those stretchers that had the bodily wounded in, those without legs and arms. No more blood-soiled blankets I noticed. Segregation had begun. I was given a mug full of tea and two tablets and when I awoke I was in a newly fitted out hospital ward.

The entire hall was filled with rows and rows of beds. But unfortunately not all of the beds was being occupied. Those men who were in bed were very still. But those that weren't were running up and down the passageways crying and shouting, salivating at the mouth and being pursued by frenzied doctors and nurses armed with syringes and other accoutrements. It was indeed a madhouse and suddenly I didn't want to be in it. Some of those young bodies had no clothes on or were tearing off what clothes they had on frenziedly as they ran.

Once caught and quickly sedated by syringe those naked bodies were being carted back to their beds and given more dozes of medication no doubt to ensure that they would stay there. Some of those who were running up and down were harder to catch than others and had to be manhandled back. But once caught those doctors and nurses did what they had to do with as much delicacy as they dared in order to bring a little dignity to proceedings which at times must have been extremely distressing to them. Even more so to those young girls who had been hurriedly drafted in as auxiliary nurses. Would I get like that . . . ? I began to wonder. I hoped not. So I just closed my eyes and tried to shut it all out but I couldn't.

Some of those boys were hardly old enough to be described as battle hardened. Yet they may have to contend with all this and perhaps a lot more for the rest of their lives. For that's what it was. It was border-line insanity. It could only be hoped that medicines and tender care could keep at least some of us on the right side of that fine line. For I was one of them. I wasn't so stupid as to think I wasn't. I may not have been so far gone as some of those poor kids. But I'd heard a doctor say that it was a progressive thing. So complacency would never be a bed-fellow of mine. Some of those wasted young soldiers not much older than boys were jumping up and down on top of their beds urinating and defecating uncontrollably as they screamed and ranted. It was bad enough for me even although I was just lying there watching it all take place. It was then that I now knew for certain that this was some sort of crazy place.

I was right about it being some sort of clearing house. But now all my worst fears had been realized. Oh it was a clearing house alright, but it was a special clearing house for the shell-shocked and the bomb-happy. Call it what you will. But that's what it was. Oh they could call it a psychiatric unit if they wanted to. Indeed this was a word that was being bandied about for the first time. But to me who had never known better, it was an asylum. And suddenly I wanted out of that place.

The whole thing was a sickening sight to behold. Some, those who were too strong physically to be held down were strapped to their beds with broad leather bands and weren't released even for basic toilet requirements.

Was this extreme cruelty? Perhaps it was. But surely it was better to change a soiled bed sheet than bury a nurse or a doctor. For some of those wasted young bodies had become criminally disturbed too.

Some just sat on their beds stark naked staring at the walls, those who weren't lying flat out on their beds that is. To an onlooker those shouts and screams would appear to be going un-noticed. But that most certainly was not the case. People were doing something about it, people who cared deeply. And those dedicated doctors and nurses were those people. The care and attention they were giving those apparently young men was wonderful to behold. They were prepared to bring a professionalism to a condition they themselves probably didn't know an awful lot about at that time. And some of us like myself who were still to be diagnosed could only lie there, and look on and wonder.

And all this in such a short space of time too. For the pace of the war together with the surge of the Allies through France, Belgium and Holland, had increased to such an extent that one got the impression that the whole Army Medical Corps had lost the place entirely and was in a state of absolute chaos. So much so that doctors, nurses and field orderlies just did not have the time to take stock let alone take time to tend the dead and the wounded. Hence the mix-ups. It was all perfectly understandable even to a cynic such as me. Pandemonium reigned day and night in that one-time monastery. And I suspected it would be a place I was going to be in for some time yet. I could only hope I was wrong. The nights not surprisingly were the worst.

The shouts, the screams and the sobs of those young wasted bodies were unending. I would lie back in the half-dark and listen. In between screams some of them would leap from their beds hoping to escape it all. I could hear the scud of their bare feet as they raced past the beds and along the corridor. And even in the near gloom I could sometimes discern the chases by the doctors and nurses. And I would listen to the catching of the poor young souls and the ensuing gasps as the needles and more medication was pumped into them.

"Jungle Juice," an orderly said the medication had been dubbed. Some might smirk and call it that. But what ever it was it was all a very horrifying and levelling experience for everyone and not just for those wasted young bodies. The pattern was the same night after night. It was all so easy to lull oneself into a kind of selfishness with regards to one's lack of sleep and the inability to get peace.
It was then quickly brought home to me that for some of those youngsters peace would never ever be. I began to wonder. Was it selfish of me to hope and pray that maybe just maybe, I wasn't as far gone as some? And that those doctors and

nurses had got me just in time to cure me? Was it right of me to be having these kind of thoughts? Rightly or wrongly those were the kind of things that beset me as I lay there night after night in my bed, because assessment hadn't yet came my way and I still wasn't all that sure if I wanted it to either.

I'd also heard it said that the body was easier to heal than the mind. This was fuelled even more by what I had heard through a haze from two medics who were standing over me in that R.A.P. as I fought my way back to consciousness. "Delayed reaction," one was saying as he shone a torch in my eyes. "Difficult to say," the other was murmuring. What exactly had they been saying about me I wondered? Was there something lying dormant inside me just ticking away? Or was there something in my head about to explode at any moment?

Or was I just being paranoid? Was it something they reckoned was just another offshoot of this particular disease. Or was I just being selfish again. I closed my eyes and tried to feel for those poor young men who already were in torment, and not to think too long and hard about myself. And what of those closest to those wounded, yes, those wounded young men? What would they say to their mothers or their sweethearts if and when they could ever got home? Apologize for not being heroes, or just sorry for not being able to stop themselves from running away. But then that's the way it was in that place.

There was a story going round as I recall which reinforced the state of flux that predominated at that time. German soldiers were being treated there too for wounds because there was no place else for them to go. French, Dutch, and Belgian soldiers were all there amongst the rest. It could only be true and only served to underline the pace and acceleration of everything round about that time. Speed was the order of the day. Doctors, nurses, and stretcher-bearers, were being literally run off their feet trying to cope with other people who ironically couldn't themselves cope. At times you began to wonder who was or indeed if anyone was running the show.

With all my heart and soul I could identify with those poor unfortunate young men in that hospital, especially those who had been caught running. Nor did I think I would be alone in saying that. There appeared to be so many facets to this shell-shock thing, and so many manifestations. There were also too many unanswered questions that made it so terribly frightening to all concerned.

There was the type of victim who merely gesticulated wildly and who tried to draw you to them to explain their plight. Those were the better ones, the saner sides of shell-shock if you like. If indeed the words better and saner were permissible.

But let us not forget either the criminality that took root in some of those wasted young bodies just because their nervous systems were unable to cope. And whose fall on the wrong side of that dividing line would be deemed unforgivable.

For some of those unfortunates had now become the criminally insane. There was no other word for it. They had attacked nurses and doctors with knives and implements and anything else they could lay their hands on. And they would never be forgiven for it. A special room now housed those few who were under special guard. Yet prior to all that they had been innocent, inoffensive young men whose only crime was to be in a place of war that had shattered their nervous systems irreparably. They had taken the only way out available to them. And had run away from it all. They had committed that cardinal military sin. To coin a phrase, they had "Deserted In The Face Of the Enemy." They would be sneered at and could well be court martialled for this most heinous of crimes.

There were other aspects too; those patients stricken dumb by the sudden shock caused by their condition; poor souls who would try to speak by twisting their already nerve-damaged mouths as far as they could, working their jaws in a desperate effort to speak trying to make sense but with no words coming out. Comparisons may be odious but as far as I was concerned they were the ones to be pitied just as much as the man who'd had both legs blown off. "Wh-y m-me?" those twisted jaws were trying to ask you. "Wh-why c-can't I g-go h-home?" " Wh-ere's my unit?" "Wh-ere's m-my mates?"

These were the questions a lot of young men were asking but no one was answering. Not a doctor. Not a nurse, there wasn't even a god to tell them. And that's the way they would see it, and I would stand alongside them on that. For I couldn't tell them either. I could have told them that I might well have joined them out there in the field if I hadn't been chopped down beforehand. But I didn't. But I nearly did. Or maybe I was just too ashamed to be one of them. Or perhaps it was just a matter of categorisation. I was with them, yet I was not with them. But I most certainly was with them in that awful place those awful nights. I was totally with them. But I wished and prayed to God that I wasn't.

Despite the frenetic segregation of the wounded, and "the walking dead" I still hadn't been assessed. No one had come near me. Was I diseased? Or was I merely a unique case? Perhaps my running wasn't up to scratch? If I was not a runner, then who or what in hell was I?

Then to cap it all, no pun intended, who should enter our ward but the soldier's friend. Everyone's friend and I don't think. None other than our very royal, our very Royal Military Police. Or the highly polished Redcaps that's who. And to many, an enemy almost as much as the Germans were to the serving soldier. And they were here especially to see those cringing bomb-happy bastards who were in that hospital masquerading as soldiers.

A fine body of men coming in to see another fine body of men salivating at the mouth and jumping helplessly up and down on their beds and running all around the place for that's what they were to see, that and a few "deserters" hopefully. Did they did really want to see young grown men gesticulating instead of speaking and who preferred making signs to making conversation? Is that really why they had come? Or was it something else? Perhaps they had received complaints about the noise those bomb-happys were making? Or was it just to gloat?

Some of those damaged young soldiers were more frightened than ever when those M.P.'s entered the ward. I know, for I was there when they came in one night. Some patients began sobbing and screaming as soon as they entered. A pair of them stood for a minute by my bed and looked down at me as I lay there. I looked up and tried to look as smug as them. Perhaps they'd been told that I hadn't been assessed yet and was therefore unpredictable. Maybe even capable of shooting their red caps from their pretty heads. Nothing was yet known about me. Better safe than sorry. Maybe they'd been briefed before and knew exactly the type they were looking for.

They walked further up the ward one nudging the other as they went. Stopping here, pointing there, and smirking. They most certainly were not driven by compassion, in visiting what in their estimation would be the "bomb-happy" afflicted I imagined by the look on their faces. Nor was it to console. No. No. They had obviously heard of this new "disease" and how it got you away from all the fighting. And they were just curious to see where we were all housed. It was obvious they didn't want any fighting either. All they sought was some fertile material and perhaps have a little bit of harmless fun. The younger ones would do nicely.

I watched as the pair of them strutted up and down the ward. I knew well what they were looking for. They were looking for young soldiers who in their estimation had ran away from the line and somehow you got the impression that they would just love to find one such person right there. They knew exactly what they were looking for and they were not going to be kept back from carrying out their duty and most certainly not by any soft pussy-footing syringe-carrying doctors who would fall all too readily for those stories about them being ill and shocked by shells. They were bloody cowards! And they would know wouldn't they, those stalwart upright M.P.s who knew their "King's Rules And Regulations" inside out as well as knowing how to keep well away from the war zones too, some would say.

And they would find those "Pretenders" as they called them. Make no mistake about that. But they were not welcome those so-called policemen of the army. They were bastards. Not all maybe, but most of them. I mean they weren't really conscripted into being an M.P., were they? Anyway I had still to meet a good one! Who did they think they were? No one wanted to be there in that place. Most of them would gladly have gone back up the line rather than lie there. You would think that even with their level of mentality that they would see that. But then again maybe they didn't want to know that. I heard one of them sniggering to a young soldier who was standing up in his bed shaking like a leaf. "Who's the Eric Liddell then? Who's the fastest runner then, eh? Was it you?" Then the other, a sergeant, the worst kind of M.P., sneered. "Out to break the fucking world record for running were we . . . ?"

But they didn't get it all their own way those Redcaps. Some of the bed-bound sick; those who could manage a few words began to fight back with faltering but nevertheless fighting talk. "We couldn't all be f-fucking back in Antwerp d-drinking t-tea and l-ladelling out s-soup in th-the c-canteen like y-you bastards, c-could we!"

Then another stuck his oar in for good measure. "Or be s-six feet t-tall, and g-get an-nice new h-hat to walk about in behind the l-lines" And as he finished his outburst he then hurled a walking stick that caught the sergeant in question right across the nose from which blood spurted out like a fountain. All this to bursts of applause from the entire ward, including myself. And as a large handkerchief was produced to stem the flow of blood, another bed-bound patient hissed. "B-by the way w-we forgot to tell you th-that he h-had b-been labelled d-dangerous. And sh-ould have been in the sp-special ward for the criminally insane but but th-they d-didn't have enough r-room f-for him . . . "

It was at that point a doctor and nurse came running up the ward to see what the trouble was all about. The incensed sergeant was still mopping blood from his nose and began shouting that he would be submitting a report to his commanding officer. The doctor had obviously sized up the situation for himself and told the sergeant to do just that. The doctor in charge retaliated however by saying that he too would be taking statements from his patients to get to the bottom of it all. With that the two MPs marched but quickly out of the ward. I got the impression somehow that no more would be heard of the incident.

The unwarranted intrusion of those Redcaps had exacerbated the conditions of some of the more serious casualties. Especially those who had bad memory losses and they shouted out and screamed incessantly all through the night. As I lay back on my bed that night I tried and tried to get my own head right. Some things were improving, but within my own body I felt somehow reduced as a man and only marginally better than some of the sad cases I saw around me in that hospital.

But I thanked my God every night for that margin. And how would they assess me I wondered? For it surely couldn't be long before I was brought before whoever it was you went before and who could tell you where your head was. What particular category would they fit me into I wondered, that is if such a category ever existed.

The constant running of those tortured young men continued well into the night. I listened as ever to them being caught and I would listen again to them being sedated where caught. And I would listen again and again to their gasps as the medication took over once more. I would then close my eyes and I would hear in the distance the sepulchral tones of what must have been those monks whose austere lives had also been turned upside down by war. And I would identify with those litanys and responses. Their dirge-like chants all added to the abject hopelessness felt by all. If you hadn't been there, and knew in your heart and soul that it was all very real you could well have believed that the whole show had been staged and choreographed by Satan himself.

Everyone, including the nurses, was still angry over those Redcaps who had tried to bully we unfortunates that night. After all as one patient had already said the only difference between them and us was that they were all six feet tall and we weren't. For who was to say what they would have done in the circumstances of war. Well turned out with their uniforms they may well have been but who was to say they were well enough turned out for battle. No one! Not even their C.O. But then that was the kind of mentality that was around in Holland in those days. At least I think it was Holland. It could quite as easily have been Belgium. For to this day I'm not quite sure. But there was a saying doing the rounds at the time that said it all. And that saying was, "I'm alright Jack!"

I was assessed a few days later and I can assure you there were no Redcaps in attendance. An officer sat me down then told me I had been very lucky. It was obvious that he had never been in that hospital. He then proceeded to tell me what had happened to me and he read it all out from a sheet of foolscap on the desk in front of him.

Apparently our Vickers-carrying Bren carrier had received a direct hit from an enemy eighty-eight during the battle of Overloon. This had resulted in my being catapulted from the carrier and against a tree thus rendering me unconscious for an unspecified length of time. But estimated to be about three hours. There was no evidence of any brain damage so far. But it was early days. I had been found by stretcher bearers in that field in Overloon who had then carried me by stretcher to an R.A.P.

Pieces of shrapnel had grazed my scalp on the right hand side of my forehead had not penetrated but were just discernible. Otherwise I would have been killed outright. It took no high-ranking officer to work that one out. I was glad that he had said that I'd been taken by stretcher to that R.A.P. At least I now knew that I hadn't actually run there. But then again maybe I should have ran away from it all as I felt like doing at the time. That way I would have been better placed to have given more moral support to those young men I had been housed with for those past few weeks. I may even have been able defend them more vigorously against the cruel jibes some ignorant people were slandering them with.

"And what about the rest of the crew," I asked anxiously. He shook his head. "I'm sorry. We just don't know yet. Early days yet and all that. But we will try to keep you informed the moment we hear anything further. Tomorrow you will appear before doctors specially trained to deal with your particular form of injury. So for the moment, that is all. And I wish you good luck."

Outside, I fingered my forehead. Imperceptible he had said, but it was very much there. Perhaps I had been lucky. It was easy for him to say. But at least I knew a little of what had happened that awful night in Overloon. Were they all still around, I wondered? There was a story too going round that the Allies were forging forward in Holland and getting ever nearer and nearer the Rhine. It was heart warming to know that our lot at least might have played some small part in that advance. I hoped and prayed to myself that they'd managed to make it despite my letting them down.

But I still felt reduced despite all the other good news I was hearing. And I would have no hesitation in saying so at my assessment if I ever got the chance to speak, that is. Next day I was given a full going over by a doctor. He shone a torch into my eyes. I was then made to stretch my hands out in front of me, and to close my eyes. This I had to do for a full minute. He wanted to test my powers of co-ordination he said. Then for some inexplicable reason he got up from his chair and left me sitting there all on my own. So there I was, all alone in a room with just a clock ticking away loudly on the wall to keep me company.

It must have been at least half an hour I'd been sitting there before he came back into the room. He made no reference to me regarding his absence but just sat reading the notes in front of him. "Does your head still ache?" he then asked. "Yes," I said. I almost went on to say. "And your shooting out the room every five minutes doesn't help things either." But I thought discretion the better part of valour here and refrained. I wanted the whole thing over as quickly and, for my part, as painlessly as was humanly possible.

He then informed me that I should prepare myself for recurring headaches. They would be severe at first but should gradually ease off. He would be less than truthful if he said I would make a complete recovery. A lot would depend on myself. But I didn't want to spoil the party by telling him that my head was not in accord with his prognosis. For at that very moment my head was throbbing fit to burst. He also pointed out that there would be times when my vision would be blurred. But there would also be bouts of severe depression, which I would also have to learn to live with. Such attacks would be controlled by medication.

This very special medication he stressed that had been administered to me in hospital and to which I had been responding to satisfactorily would require to be taken by me for the foreseeable future and maybe even for the rest of my life. All heart-warming stuff this certainly was for me. "Now do you have any questions for me?" he asked laying down his pen and looking straight at me. I tried to measure his stare and asked. "Are you saying that if I don't take the medication that is prescribed I can go crazy and maybe commit some horrible crime?"

"Not at all. You have been assessed as being a non-violent man. This I may say has not been a hasty decision by our people. You may not have noticed it whilst under medication in hospital but you have been monitored during your whole stay here. And as you yourself have probably seen there are varying degrees of this battle fatigue syndrome from which you have and still are suffering. It would be less than honest of me to say that we know a lot about this type of illness. Because we don't."

There was again a strained silence as he resorted once more to the papers before him. I sat for a while as he read. He went on again about how well I had responded to the treatment I had received in that newly formed hospital I'd been in. And weren't those doctors and nurses doing a grand job. I would certainly agree with that. All in all things had gone to plan. And with a lot of root and care there was no reason why I shouldn't make a moderate recovery. But there was still a certain amount of unpredictability about the condition.

"What's the name given to this condition of mine, doctor?" I asked. I appeared to have taken him by surprise. "I, I'm sorry but I'm not equipped to answer that one. The doctors next door will deal with you now. Goodbye once more and good luck for the future." He shook me firmly by the hand. But I was still somewhat suspicious. All this positive thinking and bonhomie was beginning to stifle me.

I was then taken next door where sat three distinguished looking officers. I was impressed. Not because they were distinguished looking but because there wasn't as much as a mark on them or their uniforms. They looked as though they all had been freshly scrubbed and parachuted in for my benefit. One in particular, a lieutenant "Colonel Blimp" type with a bristling moustache and all that stuff as I recall.

He addressed me first after consulting the notes in front of him. "How are you within yourself, Fusiliah?" he asked me fatuously. "I don't understand the question, sir." I replied. Nor did I. He had obviously done a little research had our Colonel Blimp. For he didn't call me Private. Nor did he address me as Gunner, because a gunner is what they called a private in the artillery. And he obviously knew that, no sir, no flys on our colonel . So I followed up quickly with another rejoinder. "I don't quite know what you mean, sir?"

He turned to his notes again. "I - I mean now that you're no good for Front Line duties. What sort of job would you like?" I was sorely tempted to reply. "One like yours." But I resisted the temptation. "Don't know sir, but b-but I know that there's bound to be some good ones about. "His mouth closed all of a sudden. He looked at me fixedly. His eyes narrowed. Was this cheeky chappie of a soldier being sarcastic you could almost hear him thinking. The moustache bristled just a little more. I looked straight ahead. Perhaps this bomb-happy lark wasn't going to be so bad after all.

A somewhat open-mouthed colonel then handed gladly, I thought, the questioning over to the other pair, a captain and a second lieutenant. Did I consider myself to be a good soldier? And if so did I enjoy being a good soldier? I answered in the affirmative to what I considered both silly questions. Had I always been of a nervous disposition? Again I was tempted. But resisted.

Then came the piercing ones. "Did anything unusual ever happen to you as a youth?" asked the captain. "No, sir but occasionally I got lucky." Then the second lieutenant not to be outdone after consulting his notes. "Did you enjoy being a machine gunner?" "No," I replied. "And why didn't you enjoy your role as a machine gunner?" Not one muscle on my face moved as I replied. "Because I enjoyed being a rangetaker better sir for that was my job." Another hasty reference to notes here.

I was getting the whole querulous treatment now. They were looking for flaws in my replies. They were also looking for wounds they could see. And they weren't seeing any. They weren't prepared to see what to them was a physically fit individual like myself walk out of that room and in their eyes walk away from the war too. I had answered their questions but I was getting the impression that they were only interested in their own questions rather than my answers. There was one question however I would have willingly answered without fear or favour. "Would you be prepared to go back up now to the Front Line?"

I would have replied "Certainly but I intend to take you three bastards with me so as you can tell your grandchildren you were actually there and knew what it was all about!"

I sat perfectly still but at the ready as they whispered amongst themselves. Occasionally they would look up to see if I was still there. Nor would it have surprised me if there wasn't another one of them under the table looking or not looking for twitches and reflexes. Their confab lasted about five minutes. I knew for a clock to my right was ticking away loudly. I then received their deliberations.

Their diagnosis was that I was suffering from a condition known as "Psycho - Neurosis ( Anxiety State ) as a direct result of enemy action. I would therefore be downgraded from a healthy A1 to an unhealthy B1. I would be no longer fit for Front Line duties. I bit my lip on hearing this and tried to accept with an attempt at stoicism their recommendations. I don't think.

"Colonel Blimp "apologized for the rough treatment they had given me but some cases referred to them had not been genuine, he told me in what I thought was in confidence. I didn't know whether to be pleased or offended . . .

"That's why you were left alone for half an hour. You probably didn't know it but you were under constant supervision. Doctors, especially psychiatrists have been known to be caught out in the past you know." Thanks for nothing I thought to myself. Good to know I was the real thing, a genuine dyed-in-the wool psycho. "A head case" in other words. "You will be told to report to a holding unit in due course. I wish you luck." He shook my hand and I left. It was over . . .

Deep down I thanked God that I was out of it even if it was just for the present. I had no idea where I would be going. But I wouldn't have minded going back up there to the line, Psycho or not if I thought it would have helped Smithy and the rest of the squad. Although knowing him he would probably have said, "Take your chance when you get it and run you Scotch bugger!"

I was glad to leave that awful place. Of course I was glad. Yet deep down there were still regrets. I had this strange feeling of guilt within me about leaving those tortured kids still in there with those internal head wounds. Especially the ones who couldn't explain to the world what had befallen them. Somehow it savoured of desertion my leaving them still in there facing more jags and injections. And even worst having to leave them to face still more indignities when ever they got out, at the hands of some ignoramuses of which sadly to say there were plenty.

Because there were many tortured young men still in there in that awful place waiting and waiting to be classified.

Classified as what, I kept asking myself. Some of those classified would never be right that is true. There were some who may well respond to treatment and with loads and loads of help may be able to live out their fragile hold on life for a little while. But many more would succumb, never having made it even to full adolescence. For many of them were mere boys. Even volunteers who had joined up and had lied about their age just to get the chance to fight for their country. How were they to know that later on they wouldn't be able to "measure up" to quote the Colonel Blimps of this world. But to be truthful, did any of us know . . . ?

I was being posted to a holding unit in Ostende to await further orders. But before leaving for there I went back to take my leave of the hospital I'd been in for three weeks or more. And I went purposely round each ward to thank personally and individually every doctor, every nurse and every orderly for all the care and devotion they had shown me through those stressful days and nights. And for all the patience they had given to each and every one of us.

I also went round every single bed to every patient conscious or unconscious and bade them goodbye and good luck. Because they were going to need it out there in that tear-away, unforgiving world that awaited them. For there were many youngsters still in there who were in the same state as they were when they had come in, and for the majority, that would never ever change despite all that loving care and attention.

They were just lying there waiting their turn to be taken back home. No one was to blame for the delay in getting them back. It was just an indication of how things were, around that time. Hospitals and institutions in the U.K. were just unable to cope with the demand for beds. It may sound cruel and it was. But understandably, preference was being given to soldiers, sailors and airmen who were bodily wounded but who may well recover to fight again another day. For that was the way of it.

There was still a big question mark over those who could walk, however twisted those walking bodies may be. But their time surely would come. And they would be ready to come home whether home was indeed home or merely some bleak institution tucked away out of sight in Britain's plush countryside. But their loved ones would be there to try to ease their burden no matter where. And that surely was the main thing. Because at least they would be home again regardless of the locale. And despite their despair most would settle for that.

Seventy per cent of the young men who had been in there with me would never ever regain their sanity. Those were the thoughts that engulfed me as I prepared to take my leave. And were only some of the things that would temper my joy as I packed my kit-bag ready for the road. It is true that some soldiers may have had a greater capacity than others for withstanding everything that was thrown at them, but alas all of us weren't built the same. Therein lies the answer, for if we were all the same then there would be no need for hospitals like the one I had just left . . .

It would also be true to say that those same men who could withstand all the bombs, all the mortars, and all the shells, were very brave men who had faced their death willingly for king and country in that war outside. No one was disputing that but other forms of oblivion were taking place behind those grey hospital walls, for inside that place there was a death every bit as dire . . .

## Chapter Three

*Life Aboard But Only Just*

I arrived in Ostende with my other fellow displaced persons to await orders. They were all new faces to me in that H.U. A holding unit was nothing more than an adequate overnight stay for servicemen coming back from leave or going on leave, and for many other reasons. It was a sort of melting pot or central meeting place for those coming away from the Front Line and those poor sods going back to the Front Line. And you could tell from those faces the ones who were coming and the ones who were going back. The one good thing about a holding unit was that there you got a makeshift kind of shower, a palliase and two blankets. Life savers!

It was also a place well known by us all where all the 42 Uppers and Downers had to stay before rejoining their units after having had their requisite number of penicillin jags. If you were going for your jags you were on the code known as the 42 Up. And if you'd already had your jags and you were going back you were on the 42 Down. Why it was ever called that I'll never know. But it was 48 hours for Gunn and 72 for Syph. It was also known tongue-in-cheek as a very select place strictly reserved for "People Who *MATERED!*" No guarantees. But with the new miracle drug penicillin a 90 per cent success rate was on offer and which reinforced that old scholastic adage of the "PEN" being mightier than the "SORE"!

Nor was it unknown for troops on a forty-eight-hour leave from the Front Line to head for Paris and Brussels or Antwerp to be doing the brothels hoping perhaps to cop a packet so that their return could be delayed that little bit longer. And who would blame them? But then again I never knew anyone who ever did. Then we were hit with really bad news. And it came to us over the tannoy. "All leave has been cancelled temporarily, and this we regret. Needless to say this decision has been forced upon us by circumstances. Only leave of a compassionate nature will be granted. Stand by for further announcements."

And that was that. Something else hit on the head. Passion pleas would not be entertained. The message was greeted with boos and jeers from the milling throngs of squaddies, sailors, and airmen, all caught up in this latest cross fire of red tape. All of a sudden the protest chants opened up loud and clear, stentorian stuff and as out of tune as ever "Why Are We Waiting . . . Why Are We Waiting . . . Why . . . Oh . . . Why Oh . . . Why . . . "

It was then I was called in to the Unit Orderly Office and told that I would be going back to England. Woking in Surrey to be exact. There I would be given a course on touch-typing. I remember my look of askance at the time. "touch-typing?

What in the hell's that?" They soon put me out of my misery. "Touch- typing is a new and faster way of learning how to type" the orderly room clerk told me. "But why me?" I asked.

"Because you're B.1. that's why. And you and some others in the same grade have been picked for this Course." I still didn't see the need to cancel leave and all that. "But why all the rush?" I asked innocently enough, I thought. "Because we're expecting the war to end very soon. And we need trained typing clerks to help process all the service mens demob, that's what." I was told curtly. And they should know when it was all going to end, shouldn't they? Those Desk-jockeys toughing it out back there in Woking, England . . .

And so to Woking it was for three whole weeks. Good grub. Well, as good as you would get in the army. I felt guilty. To make matters easier there was a mobile cinema in town. A luxury indeed. And Pathe News was there nightly to keep us all up to date about what was going on in Europe, and the news was good. We had crossed the Rhine and the Eleventh Armoured together with the Guards Armoured were actually on German soil. The end was surely in sight I thought. Rumours were rife. Hitler was dead. It hadn't been confirmed. But the rumours kept coming. He had been shot by some of his hench-men. I hoped and prayed the rumour was not a rumour. But we would have to wait and see.

We waited. But sadly it was only that - a rumour. But there was also talk that Hitler had withdrawn troops from Holland and Germany to try and stop the Russians from counter-attacking in Russia. And it apparently was not working out for him. This was even better news. It could spell the beginning of the end. Things were certainly going on a pace. No doubt about that. My head was beginning to spin once more. Just when I was beginning to feel alive again too.

Pathe News could hardly contain themselves as they spat it out to us from the silver screen. Hand-to-hand fighting just outside Hamburg. The Germans were surrendering in droves. The Pathe News commentator said it all and for once I forgave him those sonorous tones straight from the Noel Coward School when he ended his piece thus: - "Yes folks. The next message you hear from me might be. IT'S All OVER FOLKS!" And how right he was. For a week later it was all over. Germany had surrendered to General Montgomery. We could hardly take it in. But it appears Monty could. And did.

One week after our typing course ended I was told with some others that there would still be no leave. Instead I would be heading for Germany to assist in setting up a Military Government. Then right out of the blue and to my utter amazement I received a V.I.P. letter from the king no less. And in that letter he told me that I had been awarded the Military Medal for bravery. My immediate thoughts were that the whole thing was a sick joke. Maybe some other bomb-happy merchants had received one too. So I checked around. Not only could I not find any others who had received such a letter. But I couldn't find any other psycho neurotics types either. I was unique then in some respects.

I sat down and read the letter over and over. I then received another letter from the War Office. They regretted that I couldn't be decorated personally by the king because my whereabouts were top secret. And then to crown it all I got a letter from my father telling me about my award in case I didn't already know. He didn't know where I was either. I didn't exactly know myself where I was. The whole thing was in danger of becoming too much for me. My father went on to tell me that our local paper *The Eastern Standard*, had written a big piece about me together with a photograph of me on the front page. They were making me out to be a Local Hero. My head was spinning again.

Shortly afterwards I heard that only two decorations had been awarded for that assault on Overloon. A Welsh sergeant in the Tank Regiment who had been fighting alongside myself and others in that hellish field in Holland had been awarded the Victoria Cross. And for some unknown reason I had also been awarded the next best award i.e. The Military Medal. The sergeant had received his for valour in the field. Mine for bravery in the field. It had all to do seemingly with stopping the rot and making way for the advance on the Rhine. The sergeant had managed apparently to get into that signal box after our machine guns had softened them up. I remembered him. But I remembered nothing more. That's when I must have been chopped down.

Although I remembered that sergeant and some of his crew I never quite got to know his name. Nor do I suppose he ever got to know mine. But I'm sure he deserved that most coveted of awards, the V.C. If the full story of that battle was ever told perhaps I would be deemed not to be worthy of my humble M.M. I don't know. And I don't care. Like I've said before. Medals never interested me at any time. Nor would it ever be a case of sour grapes. Because as an ardent Celtic supporter I was well used to collecting second prizes.

Or maybe I just happened to be running the right way, army wise. And someone had seen me doing so. Or perhaps I was just running, trying to escape it all. And it was all just one horrible nightmare. Maybe that sergeant and myself were both running. Who's to say anyway. I may be wrong and I hope I am. But I don't recall any officers there that night. No crisp concise orders to advance with them at the forefront. Nobody. And I'm sure Smithy and company would back me there. And there was me getting a gong for almost joining those happy band of runners. So who was to say that some of those young men who couldn't take any more, whose nerves had snapped, weren't just as entitled to a medal as me or that sergeant who I had fought beside. Maybe we were both running and happened to get our wires crossed and managed to remedy matters just in time. It was the injustice of it all that angered me and soured the whole proceedings.

So there it was and there was I. A letter of commendation from a king and a medal for bravery. Not only was I was bomb-happy. But I had in my possession a letter to prove it. That in itself should make me a good if somewhat erratic touch-typist. I comforted myself in the knowledge that I may yet be able to make myself useful if only for getting some war-weary squaddie his demob that little bit quicker. However one thing was indisputable. The war was over. Because a declaration had been read out to us all about the cessation of hostilities and the ramifications contained therein. Germany was to be occupied by the Allied forces. And that beleaguered country would be split up into zones, British, American, and Russian. It would be history in the making. But I was in no mood to make history or anything else for that matter.

So much was happening all at the one time that I felt my head was about to burst wide open. But I would have to toe the line if anything was to be salvaged for the future. So Germany it would have to be whether I liked it or not. I sat down and tried to take stock. I just wanted to go home. But I couldn't get home. No one would be getting home. It was to be a case of pulling oneself together and moving on. Where had I heard those words before? Oh yes. It was just before Overloon, from an officer just sitting across the desk assessing me . . .

The journey from the Hook of Holland to Germany didn't do anything to chase away the blues either. No one was expecting world cruise standard or anything like that. Nor did we get anything like that. What we got didn't relate to any standards.

Eventful certainly. But tinged at the same time with a fair amount of all that shouldn't happen but did. And by the looks of things boarding that boat was going to be the easy bit. Sailing her was going to be the problem. In pristine condition she certainly was not. Visions of the *Marie Celeste* immediately sprang to mind. Although to be fair it was very early days and the run from Hull to the Hook had only just closed being the forerunner of the Harwich run to the Hook Of Holland.

One suspected that even turning this antique boat would entail the supreme effort. Our suspicions were confirmed when the captain (I wasn't all that sure she'd run to a captain) announced that the journey to the Hook of Holland would take approximately thirty six hours. I jokingly checked with one of the crew that the captain had said thirty six hours and not thirty six days.

But at least that old boat despite her antiquity had sides to her unlike that little flat boat we had when we crossed the channel on the 7th of June. I was beginning slowly to feel a resurgence of the old spirit within myself once more. My sense of humour which at one time I thought I'd lost; and which I'd always prided myself in having was perhaps coming back to me again. Or was it? Then again it might just as well have been the effects of that quarter bottle of rum I'd scrounged in Woking. Or was it just the smell of that old sea air that doing it's stuff. Whatever it was that was doing it I knew not. But what it was doing for me I liked. Once aboard, a few of us wandered round that old ship trying to drink in her doubtless glorious historic past.

The poop deck had been reserved for a few hundred German P.O.W.s who were being allowed home to the Fatherland under heavy guard by our old friends the M.P.s. And they did it so well. A large notice stood at the bottom of the steps to the poop deck "Entry Forbidden." It didn't present a problem to us since most of us had seen a German close up. Close enough to see what a German soldier looked like. Unlike some . . .

And as though to prove that they were just as human as anyone else those German prisoners entertained the entire ship's company by singing lustily and tunefully in the damp night air. They sat together huddled up on the top deck blissfully unaware that they were not included in that night's guest list. Because it had just been leaked to us that our very good friends in the Army Catering Corps were already preparing some gastronomic delights for us below decks . . . The menu was pinned up on the notice board just beside the ship's galley. And it was with both anticipation and relish that I read what they had in store for us. Only the Yanks could have afforded this I thought; -

1st Course : Pea Soup or Sardines On toast.
2nd Course; Irish Stew with Dumplings.
3rd Course : Rhubarb Tart and Custard.

It was all mouth-watering stuff. No doubt about that. Or was it Marshal's "Lease Lend" gone mad? I wondered. Could well have been. Or was it now that the war was finally over just a case of our much-maligned A.C.C. trying to win us all over?

Then just as we were smacking our lips to let us know we were still in the army we were hit hard with Part Two Orders pinned up just below the menu. "All troops will be positioned by 21.30 hours to participate in the aforesaid meal. Thereafter there will be a session of housey-housey, presided over by the Duty N.C.O. It is hoped all personnel will attend."

Then an afterthought in case we got lost. "The canteen where festivities will commence is situated immediately adjacent to the ship's galley." And then another sweetener, "Hot Cocoa," (Was there any other kind?) "and biscuits will be provided for those participating in housey-housey. Lights Out, 23.00 hrs. Goody goody," we all said to a man. Good food and late beddy byes. How lucky could you get! They were obviously preparing us for Civvy Street and no mistake. We would all say "Amen" to that.

After our tour of the ship most of us went below to make up our two-tiered bunk beds just in case the jollification's lined up for us rendered us incapable of doing it later. We also wanted the rest of the evening to ourselves. We read books. We played cards. We also talked of home and of war and of the occupation of Germany in which some of us were about to be a part. I still couldn't see myself as a touch-typist however much I tried. Then as the witching hour for our food bonanza approached our old ship began to flounder just a little . . .

There was nothing to get hysterical about. It was just a little turbulence we were assured by the ship's crew. But somehow they didn't sound too convincing. Then came an unmistakable lurch to starboard. This time it was even more pronounced. But give that crew their due, despite our colliding into one another, being thrown against each other and at times falling on top of each other as we tried to walk around we were assured from the Bridge that everything was O.K.

There was nothing to worry about. Then it came over the loudspeaker, "All troops will report to B Deck immediately for boat drill!" So off we all tripped to B Deck and performed our boat drill. "Purely a precautionary measure" the announcement assured us. But it did not assure me or any others, come to think of it.

The list certainly began to ease off just a little as we finished our drill. But for some the damage had been done. And I had to say I was one of them despite those reassurances from the bridge. Because there was still a bit of a swell in the ship's movement. It was a kind of movement that made me feel distinctly queasy. And I made an on the spot decision to forego the promised feast ahead much as the pangs of hunger mourned within me. Somebody up there didn't like us and I didn't mean those German P.O.W.s up on that poop deck either.

I opted for bed instead. Not one of my best decisions either for the bed began to move and my stomach with it. But for some of those brave souls the thought of all that food was just too much and some were already heading for the canteen. Just lying in your bunk could be roughly equated to someone pushing you from the rear on a swing only in this case you didn't somehow need that push if you know what I mean. I tried to shut any thought of food from my mind and managed to get a couple of hours sleep instead.

I awoke then instantly wished I hadn't. Bodies clad in string vests and army issue "drawers cellular, for the use of were streaming towards doors which bore a sign above them in three languages "Gents," "Senors," and "Les Hommes". I looked at my watch. Twelve o'clock. There was a lot of moaning and groaning and cellular drawers round the ankles crouched at the ready. The floors of our deck was awash with urine, vomit and semi-solids. It was patently obvious that there were some who hadn't quite made it the "Gents," "Senors" or even to "Les Hommes".

The place stank to high heaven. Meanwhile the good old S.S. "Whatsitsname" was still sloshing about somewhere in the North Sea. I carefully stepped down from my top bunk and fortunately found a dry spot. I felt I somehow had to get up on deck and get some fresh air. I managed to step gingerly past a few foreign substances and grabbed a handrail at the bottom of the steps. I noticed the handrail had been oiled by something thick too as I got up to the canteen. There was a deathly hush everywhere. Even the sea seemed to have calmed down somewhat. Slowly, very slowly, I pushed open the door of the canteen and could only stand and stare at what I saw inside. Tables were all lying together side by side as though stuck together by glue. Fragmented crockery was swilling about in pools of red liquid. H.P. sauce bottles were colliding with each other on the floor. Knives and forks were racing each other from one end of the floor to the other. There was no one to be seen. Again the name, *Marie Celeste* flashed in front of my eyes. There was no one in sight. Not one N .C.O., no one. Not even an M.P.!

In fact the only thing that was still standing was a huge aluminium urn with the tap slowly leaking a thick dark brown liquid. It was obvious that the cocoa and biscuits stage of the proceedings had not been reached. I'd seen enough and withdrew trying desperately to keep what little that was in my stomach down. I could just hear the sound of singing from the poop deck. Those bloody P.O.W.'s were still giving it laldy up there. "Wir Fahren Hohe" . . . and "Deutschland Deutschland Uber Alles," were just a few I could make out as I wended my way carefully to my bunk. What kind of songs I wondered would they be singing if they had won!

To say that we were all glad to be off that old hulk would be to put it mildly. In particular those who had partaken well if not wisely of the feast aboard that floating Festive Table. Even those who for the best part had been domiciled in the toilets for most of the trip were looking distinctly green around the gills wherever those gills were in a soldier's anatomy. One got the impression that it was a culinary experience they could have well done without.

I didn't feel all that great myself and I hadn't eaten a thing, so I felt for them. I really did. And I was glad to see the Hook of Holland, hooked or un-hooked. Believe you me. Those prisoners were still singing their heads off and unfortunately for us would continue to do so, for we were told they would be entrained with us still under guard and would be with us all the way. They were being taken back to a transit camp in Germany prior to their release. And what were they being released into I wondered. For if any of those poor sods were to see what we were to see a few hours further up the line they would have been back on that old ship in a flash and there would have been no more singing, that's for sure . . .

We were crammed into that waiting train to such an extent that there was hardly room to breathe let alone sit down. It was then we all began to wonder just who were the victors and who were the vanquished. For those prisoners at the rear of that long train were still singing and most of them were seated. Even those who weren't, had their heads stuck out of windows and were still singing as the train pulled away from the station.

I had seen Holland before and it had bad memories for me. I hadn't liked what I saw then nor what I had done there. Now I was seeing it again this time from a vertical position through the window of a train. And I still didn't like what I saw. Those small toy-like houses, looked as though they were made entirely from glass and they all had flat roofs. Glass predominated. It was obvious that the Dutch didn't much care who could see into their homes. Some of us got the impression that maybe they were designed for just such a purpose and it was a feature that was greatly appreciated especially when those young women came out on to their glass patios and waved to us all as we passed.

It was indeed very pleasing to the eye. As were those pretty little gardens of theirs. Everything was neat and tidy. You got the impression they polished the grass after they'd cut it. Or was I merely being over critical of what seemed to me to be a sanitized version of Holland because of my previous experiences there. Somehow Overloon didn't quite fit into the scheme of things. I may be wrong but that's the way I saw it. But give the Dutch people their due however they cheered us vigorously as we sped past.

But the best was yet to come. And Changing the Guard at Buckingham Palace was nothing with what we were privileged to witness further up the line. The Changing of the Guards at the Holland\German Border was a thing to savour. The train shuddered to a halt at the crossing. And everybody aboard that train flocked to the windows to observe the change - over. For this was austerity, obscenity, and what's commonly known in the army as "dumb insolence", all merged into one.

Down the steps of the vanguard the Dutch guard would stomp holding his lantern in his hand and a large book of sorts under his arm. He would then tramp further along the track to meet his German counterpart who had giant keys jangling from his belt. They would then bow stiffly to acknowledge each other's presence. And all this in complete silence. The German guard would accordingly acknowledge; bow in response, click his heels, take the proffered documents and proceed to mount the steps of the train whilst the Dutch guard would do an about turn and march back into the waiting room reserved for him on the Dutch side of the border. This indeed was acrimony personified.

The whole ceremony was over in a few minutes with not a word spoken. Then as if to atone for all the solemnity that had gone before the silence was broken by almighty cheers from watching heads thrust through the windows as we spectated at this unique, even bizarre "Handing Over Of The Guard." True, some of the cheers were tinged with jeers. But it was worth it for all that. Like that old saying? "Worth A Guinea A Box" just to observe it all. More especially from the British contingent aboard the train

Little did we know however that we would have to go through the same rigmarole again when we actually crossed the border into Germany. For along the corridor of the train came yet another German officer. This was the ticket inspector and passport officer all rolled into one. The mere fact that nobody seemed to have any tickets didn't seem to worry him at all for he bowed, heel-clicked, and even saluted at times with utter abandon as he went about his duties.

But the serious stuff really started when the train rolled into the country that it was all about. Deutschland. Once more the windows were rolled down as far as they could go as we all feasted our eyes on the offering afforded us. And a hush seemed to envelop the whole of the train. Because for most of us aboard that train this was our first baptism of the Fatherland. This indeed was Deutschland Uber Alles . Because it was most certainly "Uber" on all the faces along that corridor as we gazed and gazed.

Every window had a nose pressed against it. It was all the better if you could stick a neck out. All the better to see. And it was something to see for most of us. The small squat glass houses of Holland were no more to be seen as their gigantic warring neighbours took over from them. Not only in war either it would seem but architecturally too. Even run-of-the-mill garden huts seemed to assume a grandeur of their own. Purpose-built was a word that sprang to mind. Gothic but at times gaunt structures seemed to give us a qualified welcome as we sped on.

Gigantic barns gave off an edifice - like appearance too. Everything that could be seen from that train was bigger, better and taller than anything any of us had ever seen. Even the crops were bigger, better and more yellow than anything I had ever seen. Or maybe it just looked that way. Perhaps they were planned to look that way as a deterrent to all who would dare to think for themselves. Those crops, the barns, and even those dilapidated out-houses seemed to be shouting to us down the wind as we passed. "Anything you can do I can do better."

The train slowed as it engaged a large circular turn of the track and this enabled us all to get a more panoramic view of the whole countryside. Was that German grass really greener than our own back home? Were their crops really better and bigger than ours? Or did it just seem that way because we had just come from a country that for the past five years or so had been as austere as winter itself. Maybe our propaganda people had got it all wrong yet again. For none of those people in the fields looked starving to me as we trundled past. No skinnymilinks here I remember thinking . . .

Nothing skinny looking either about those flaxen-haired frauleins as they pitchforked hay into stacks in those fields. Nothing straggly about those golden locks that some had pleated down the backs of their necks. And the faces of those young frauleins as we passed, sullen they may well have looked, but beautiful too, most certainly. The men in the field with them looked for all the world like men in the field look like; ordinary. Very ordinary, mind you some of them looked as though they could have made good alternative uses for those pitchforks they held in their hands.

With our train almost in the shape of a large "U", we could see the back of the train and those prisoners we were carrying with us. The men and the women in the fields rose to their cheers and their shouts of "Heim," "Heim" at the top of their voices. Those prisoners may have thought they were going home. But we, we British soldiers were going to *their* homes! One couldn't help but feel just a little sorry for the poor sods. They had put everything they had into an outfit that had finally let them down by sheer bloody greed. And as they looked into each other's faces as look, I'm sure they must have done many times, they must have cursed and cursed for being so credulous as to believe all that propaganda that had been poured down their throats. And at their own readiness to gobble it all up.

What made this particular entry into Germany so special for me and unforgettable in so many ways was it's striking similarity to the South of Ireland, the Free State as it was then called. The green fields, and the small farm-holdings. Even some of their farm-houses reminded me so much of Ireland. The difference was however that the spectacle I was looking at from that train window, had a finished look to it. It possessed a high level of sophistication that Ireland didn't have. How well I remember when as a boy I was always taken to Ireland, together with my brothers and sisters for the school holidays . . .

. . . Glasgow Fair was my father's holiday time. For that was when the city of Glasgow virtually came to a halt for the Fair Fortnight. It was a city that would be more or less free of work for a full fortnight. As my father had been born in the county, Cavan, which was in the Free State of Ireland. Cavan's that's where we were all headed. Because not to have been making that annual pilgrimage to the mother country would have been tantamount to committing a mortal sin in my father's eyes.

My mother on the other hand used to take us first of all to Toomebridge in County Antrim; the Protestant North if you like. That's where my mother was born. Year in year out it was the same. First to Toombridge with my mother then off to County Cavan for the rest of the holidays. It was as though my father was on a rescue mission to take us from the Protestant North to the Catholic South. But there was nothing sinister about it. It just happened. And it happened every year. Perhaps it was all just co-incidental . . .

Or it may well have been to take my mother away from the constant drum practice of the local Orangemen as they rehearsed for the Twelfth of July. We'll "bate the drum till our knuckles bleed" they would often say. My mother would often recount to us how her Protestant neighbours would be the best in the world up until a week before the Twelfth of July. And then not a word would be spoken between them until the bonfires which would burn for that week died out. Then and only then would normal service be resumed. But then such were the vagaries and the sad deep-seated hatred of that beautiful but tortured land that was Ireland . . .

But there was none of that as my eyes tried to take this mirror image of Ireland in. Then when we were on our holidays in the twenties and thirties in Ireland we would seek out wild strawberries. We would pluck roguish and very large mushrooms from the green fields around my auntie's cottage and we would smack our lips as they sizzled on the turf fire. And we would soak up that delectable mushroom gravy with freshly baked soda bread which had been hauled in from the window sill outside, where it had been left to cool. That was Ireland then. That was Ireland the Great.

The Ireland not so great however was when you could scarcely see to read since there was no electric light. The Ireland not so great was when you disappeared into the bushes with a piece of newspaper in your hand, which you most certainly didn't take with you to read. Ireland was beautiful. But the Ireland of the thirties was primitive to put it mildly. So the Germany that was unfolding before my very eyes was the epitomé of everything I'd desired. This wasn't Deutschland. To my eyes this was Ireland with electricity and running water! . . .

But all this wasn't just about me and my thoughts of the past. This was an epoch making journey for all those aboard that train. You only had to take a look at the soldiers packed around those open windows in that train corridor to judge for yourself. The whole thing made compulsive viewing. So just drink it all in. It would be something for us all to tell our children about when we got home. For the war was over. We were the victors, and they were the vanquished. And we must never forget that. Otherwise they would take over again and make better barns, than us, better tanks than us. In fact they would go out to prove that they could do anything better than us except maybe win wars . . .

We had won the war. But winning the peace wouldn't be so easy and as though to reinforce those sentiments our little heel-clicking inspector was still sticking to his task as he wended his way in and out of compartments looking for someone's ticket to punch. Still no one had the heart to tell him that from here on in he and his little ticket-punching machine's actions could only be academic for here we were, coursing through *his* country!

Deep down, even he must have known that invading soldiers did not carry passports let alone train tickets. But he did his duties with such dedication for all that. Maybe that was the reason no one had the guts to tell him it was all over and that we had won the war. It may well be that he secretly knew they had lost. Perhaps he just didn't want to believe it!

They most certainly had a fetish for uniforms and gadgets. And when I say gadgets I mean articles like keys that jingled jangled jingled as in the song. They loved uniforms. Because uniforms signified power. They would revel even in little gadgets like ticket-punching machines that went straight through the ticket that was proffered them. There must have been times when the milder type of German civilian, (and there were some), must have thought the thing was going to be pierced right through their very own heart when they handed their ticket over to be punched.

Those Germans most certainly did not believe in pussy-footing around. No one could ever accuse them of doing that. Another thing they seemed to specialise in were "signs" as we all noticed when they had to vacate a town or village. Even in Normandy, they translated all the French signs into their own lingo. Where the French would stick up a sign like "Please put out the light when leaving." the Germans would merely stick up a notice that said : "Licht Aus!" "Lights Out!".

They didn't just believe in translating things for you either did the Huns. They transposed too. No "Please." No "Thank You." No nicetys. No "Kiss my arse." No grovelling. Nothing like that for them. Whatever traits the Germans had, ambiguity most certainly wasn't one of them. That was why they were in the position they were at the moment. The boot in the fullest sense of the word was now on the other foot alright. No longer were they centre stage. They were now reduced to being a mere side-show. Just something to look out of a train window at now and shake your head . . .

## Chapter Four

*The Fatherland*

On we surged through the Fatherland and once the green fields of the countryside were left well and truly behind we began to see for ourselves the results of our round-the-clock bombing. Devastation was total. Most of the smaller towns and hamlets we didn't know the names of because there was nothing in print to tell us anything. The few civilians we passed were actually standing higher than the brickwork around them. It was a grotesque *Gulliver's Travels* scenario, with the Lilliputians mere bundles of rubble.

Water and effluent poured uncontrollably from every available outlet spiralling ever higher and higher to flood any brick foundations that were still in place. A few German youngsters shouted and jeered at us as they stood defiant amongst the filth that was well nigh engulfing them. One got the impression however that a few of them weren't quite sure where their allegiance might eventually lie.

And again that famous slogan which the Germans had adopted especially when vacating towns in Belgium and Holland reasserted itself. A huge poster proclaimed to one and all "Wir Kommen Wieder". Whether the dissolute residents around believed them or not seemed somehow immaterial. Because the cardboard or whatever it had been printed on was now beginning to curl up at the edges through a lack of adhesive. And the message was gradually becoming lost. A case of not enough paste to make it stick perhaps, or just a case of enough is enough?

OK. So they would be back. Saying one thing and doing it were two different things; but from where we were standing it was going to be a long long time before that ever happened. For the further in we got to that torn land the more grim it became. Our train just roared past some of the smaller stations. Perhaps it was to shield our eyes from seeing too much of the damage done to that sad land and her people.

But still those young flaxen -haired kids ran alongside our train wherever and whenever they could shouting out gesticulating and defiantly treating us to jeering "Seig Heil" salutes, whilst their veteran counterparts stood by in silence sporting the absence of one limb or another. And in many cases both. I tried counting the numbers so afflicted but gave up. There were just too many. Yet still that same arrogance in nine out of ten of those gaunt faces remained. And from where I was standing it would take an awful lot to change those expressions.

I saw many a British soldier's face turn away if only briefly at times just not wanting to take it all in. There were endless halts due understandably to debris on the line.

This in itself brought us a little respite from the sights along the way. What we were watching was the total decimation of the Fatherland in their own land. And for the next few hours the halts, the jolts, the slow erratic starts by our train began to frustrate and even haunt us. Not only that but it was noticeable that queues for the vantage points at the corridor windows were on the wane too. It looked as though even the most hardened of us had seen enough.

Finally and to the great relief of us all our train limped into Hamburg's Hauptbahnhof; Hamburg's main central station. We were then told we could de-train, and move about for an hour. And believe you me we were good and ready to do just that, because there was a city out there somewhere. True it may well have been dismantled by as much as eighty per cent according to some estimates but it was a city nevertheless. And it was ours for the seeing, and if we wished for the taking too in every sense of the word.

We got off that train quickly just in case someone changed their minds. And when we did manage to get our feet on that platform we could only stand and stare at what we saw. Hamburg's Hauptbahnhof was gigantic. And although I knew that first impressions may not always be correct I figured that Glasgow Central Station together with Glasgow's Queen Street Station, themselves no rail minnows by any means could well have fitted in there side by side and there would still have been room for more. It wasn't an easy thing to estimate but that was as rough an idea of the size as you would get I reckoned.

I tried counting platforms till they ran off into the horizon and doubted if even London's Victoria could have competed alongside this Hamburg monument. Nor was it just the size of the station that first hit you. It was the high-tech splendour that made you stare open-mouthed at it all. How could such edifices be conjured up by anyone especially in those austere years between the wars?

Look up and you saw huge glass domes that had somehow evaded our continual bombings. And that gargantuan glass canopy that was the ceiling for all this, seemed to be looking down on as though chiding us and perhaps wondering what we were going to do to her next. And communication was the name of the game in Der Bahnhof. If you thought Euston or Victoria's boarding instructions for passengers fluidly enunciated by some announcer straight out of Eton were well nigh perfect then you could think again.

Adolf, possibly because he'd been caught out himself in his student years and maybe finding himself in the wrong train had obviously given this thing a great deal of thought I reckoned. There would be no blunders there caused by regional accents as far as he was concerned. One could almost visualise him saying to himself. "Zings vill change venn I am in charge!" Be it by Hitler or whoever, it was all still very impressive by any standards. And it worked.

For every single announcement that came over that loudspeaker was simultaneously flashed on to a huge screen high up beside a control tower. Even then it was clear that Der Fuhrer had the Hitler Youth in mind at the time. Because if little Heinz for some reason (and it better be a good one) was not in the Wehrmacht or the Luftwaffe, then he most certainly would not be late for ze Office. To my mind that station had everything. It was technology at it's finest. Little wonder you might think that the Germans would suddenly over-run the lethargic French or the equally indolent Dutch every so often whenever they felt like it. We even spotted a couple of double-decker trains just outside the station. Only the Germans could have come up with that one.

If this sounds all too complimentary to the Germans it must be remembered that the war was over. And the town we were talking about could have been London or Glasgow. But it wasn't. It was Hamburg, Germany, and few if indeed any of us had ever been further afield than Blackpool or Morecambe, and in my case Dunoon or Rothesay. So to most of us this was it, a new if a somewhat badly bruised world was unfolding right there in front of us. We were making history. And as far as we were concerned the only way to make an historical impact was to do something about it. For we who were on that train scarcely knew each other. We were all from different units that had been slung together to make up some sort of advance party and to take part in the occupation of Germany. And you could only tell it as you saw it.

That's why we were desperate to look around and see for ourselves. So we were split up into small groups and told to stick together whatever the circumstances. We chose to walk up the broad stairs to the street rather than ascend by the electric stairs that seemed to be over-populated with sleeping, snoring, bundles of people. Civilians and bareheaded German soldiers were draped over the handrails swigging liquor from a bottle they were passing round.

They glared over at us threateningly as we ascended. Our hands went automatically to our shouldered rifles. But the incident passed. No words were spoken. An angry drunken shout from one gesticulating member of the group was halted when he suddenly but inadvertently fell over. We moved up the stairs to the street above. "Do not get involved." That was the drill spelled out to us by the sergeant in charge. "Move about in small groups, no loners. Look, but don't touch and keep your hand on your weapons and by that I mean your rifles. No fucking heroes. Be back here in an hour. Got that . . .?" The message was unequivocal!

Above in the street it was just beginning to get dark. Piles of rubbish were lying all over the place. People just sat down wherever they could find room in the street and wept openly midst all the rubble. Children, some as young as four or maybe five years were obviously expected or possibly forced to stand, so that their elders could sit down instead and grieve in peace.

And having given up their coveted place on the pavement to their grown ups those German kids played in the muck and slime and empty shell casings that proliferated. They would chase each other in and out of burned-out vehicles that were strewn around quite oblivious of the rats that were scurrying along the pavement edges like cats. Not that there were many cats about either come to think of it. Plenty of rats, dead and un-dead, but no cats. And one could draw one's own conclusions on that one. Some sewers had collapsed under the constant bombing of the R.A.F. making even sitting places where one could just sit and weep also at a premium. This indeed was misery at it's most abject.

A few street lights flickered in and out making everything more sinister still. And as darkness descended the more inventive among them would produce paraffin lamps to prolong the light of way. But they would also pay in kind some unfortunates for the shedding of light from the aforesaid lamps. Because some unfortunates became more unfortunate than others. It was the barter system at it's most vile. For when daylight died on those streets and collateral, human or otherwise was not to hand so too did the "Shed Kindly Light" dimension. Complete oblivion in the form of total darkness would then ensue. It was something however that had become all too familiar to most of us by now.

Men and women begging for food and money and prepared to let you do anything to them to get it. It was all humbling stuff and was becoming all too embarrassing for us. We didn't know what to do. We wished they would all go away. After all, they started the bloody thing and I felt like telling them that. But what do you do when kids start tugging at your sleeve. These were the situations we would have to get used to if we were to survive our very selves.

Bugger them all I kept telling myself. They weren't going to get me down. My own body had suffered and was still suffering on account of them and I had to steel myself every so often just to keep up. So why should I feel sorrow for them? These streets we were treading could well have been London streets. They might well have been the streets of my own native city. But they weren't.

We were not in London or Glasgow. We were in the city of Hamburg. It was bloody Hamburg. And I most certainly wasn't going to let them spoil my glorious adventure or my escape if you like if I could help it. It was my earnest wish that I could make a new life for myself away from all the bullets and all the implements of war and I was going to make damned sure that those wishes of mine were granted. It was all very well saying these things, but in those god-forsaken streets anything was liable to happen to you. At least in war you knew who your enemy was. But there in Hamburg war over or not, in the failing light the whole world could be your enemy. For no one could go on watching their backs for ever.

We moved slowly along the street. Every corner spouted water and slime from manhole covers that weren't covering anything any more. Excrement littered the streets. As with cats, I didn't notice any dogs either. The stench in places was overpowering. Further along the street I noticed a small group of people in the gathering gloom. A green-coated German policeman was walking up and down, supervising a small group of civilians who appeared to be trying to sort out some bricks from the rubble of rubbish that lay all around. We stood and watched intrigued. What was it all about? What were they looking for? I decided to try out my somewhat limited German and approached the policeman.

Seeing my uniform he bowed stiffly and clicked his heels as they were wont to. I asked him the reason for all those civilians being there. And a mixed crew they there too. Some in rags, others better dressed, but all with that gaunt, haunted look. One civilian even had a dress suit on. Surely he hadn't dressed formally for this? Or perhaps he had been given the wrong directions on his way to a party?

The policeman shook his head and smiled at me then explained. Hamburg, like most other large German cities, he said, was in such a bad state due to the saturation bombing by the R.A.F that something had to be done quickly. Therefore a clean up was ordered to try to salvage whatever they could from what was left, if indeed anything had been left still standing. So his assembled squad, he went on to explain further, had all been found guilty of some minor civil offences. And besides being fined twenty or thirty marks depending on the crime committed they would be required to spend two hours per day under guard, trying to prise whole bricks from amongst the rubble. Those bricks would then be placed neatly in piles at the side of the roads as they went.

Those whole bricks would then be ready for the bricklayers to collect if and when it was decided by our military government to start re-building again. "And what about those bricks that were are quite whole?" I asked him. "What happens to them? Will they be thrown away?" He shook his head vigorously. "No. No," he replied. "They will be crushed up and mixed in with the cement so that the cement which is in short supply will last out longer." It was also noticeable that all the time the policeman was speaking and explaining to us, the maelstrom of workers under his command kept their heads down lifting and placing those bricks with the utmost dedication.

When I explained to our group about the bricks and the offenders having to lift them and place them neatly under supervision they howled with laughter. Now when I reflect on that incident all those years ago I suppose it could have been a fore-runner to what is now known today as "Community Service." Something else I suppose that those bloody Germans had thought of first I suppose. Some months later I had occasion to go back to Hamburg and saw piles and piles of those whole bricks ready and waiting to be laid yet again. It would be a prelude to the commencement of the re -building of the Fatherland. And yet in Hamburg as in everywhere else, it was still only 1946 . . .

And they would have to build and build soon because the damage done by our aerial attacks had produced in some cases complete obliteration. So great was the devastation that anyone and that included myself who had survived buzz-bomb attacks and the like whilst in London would readily admit it was nothing compared to this. For although London was a fearsome place to be in at the height of the bombing we agreed to a man that we had never ever before seen destruction that could match this.

In fact it was so bad that one of our officers seemingly tried to restrict our walk-abouts to certain areas in case our morale would be affected. To put this decimation of a city in context would be difficult. As a man Glasgow born and bred would be for me to walk from Glasgow's Trongate along Argyle Street then straight on to Anderston Cross for about a mile and a half and see nothing on either side as you walked. Or in an area such as Maryhill there would be nothing but absolutely nothing to see at all. It was as stark as that. We had spared them nothing. And who was to say they hadn't deserved every bit of it. That's as I saw it.

Despite all their knowledge and all their reputed know-how, it just wasn't enough. It was rumoured then that Hitler had lost the war when he decided to withdraw thousands of his troops from Normandy to try and capture Stalingrad. Be that as it may the fact remained that they had tried to conquer the world and had failed. They had gambled and they had lost and now the German people would have to live with that fact for the rest of their lives. After one last look round we made our way back downstairs to report back. Another curious feature was that despite the damage to the station there wasn't one scrap of paper or a piece of rubbish to be seen on any of those platforms. A sign in German read *"Achtung. Keine Dreck. Strafe Dafür."* Or for our benefit. *"Litter Louts Beware. Fines will be imposed."* Efficient to the end was our German citizen. Just before entraining one of our squad chipped a cigarette butt away then and trod on it. Just to give it that "lived - in" look!

Just before we entrained, the last one of our outfit came down the stairs to tell us that he had walked a little further along the road unknown to us. Then told us he'd wished he hadn't. He said he saw something that would haunt him to his grave. And he was no softie believe you me for I'd got to know him quite well both on ship and on the train. He said he saw a man, a woman and three young children sitting round a huge fire and beside the fire lay the skeleton of a horse with only the ears, teeth and hooves remaining. The last of the flesh was being roasted on the end of prongs, which they were holding to the flames.

Some of the children couldn't even wait till the flesh was done and were licking the gravy from the prongs as it dripped. He himself was violently sick on seeing this. When they spotted him the man got up from the fire holding a long piece of wire which he'd been using as a prong and ran towards this member of our group. And thinking he was going to be attacked he immediately drew his rifle and aimed but the man seemingly just wanted to offer his wife to him for a few cigarettes or anything else he had on him. Nothing high-tech about that I thought.

Our friend who I now believe was called Norman also told us how he had also witnessed two bow-tied violinists obviously professionals by their sound playing the sweetest of music in the street on their violins. No doubt pre-war they would have performed often for the Hitlers, the Goerings, and for the good Doctor Goebels, in Hamburg's pre war High Society ...

But now they were giving the recital of their lives by a kerbside to an audience of no one in particular, with an up-turned top hat on the ground in front of them. The whole thing was bizarre, grotesque, even. This was the Master Race we were now observing. The rise and fall of. Those two violinists, brilliant though their piece undoubtedly was, were in the process of being up-staged. For that up-turned top hat on the pavement beside them wherein a few coins lay surely said it all!

Whilst waiting for our train to pull out of Hamburg we heard that the Yanks who were occupying the Eastern Zone were rampaging through Berlin buying up everything in sight including women. That may have surprised a few of our crowd but it didn't surprise me. In Normandy it was the very same. There the Americans bought guns from us. Yes, guns. They bought Lugars. They bought all sorts. In fact they would buy any kind of German pistols they could lay their hands on. Better still if someone else could lay their hands on them for them.

But of course most of the pistols came from our own infantrymen like the Highland Light Infantry in particular. Now every soldier or nearly every soldier knows the infantrymen were invariably the most advanced troops at any given time and consequently were always first to make contact with the enemy. And in our case it was kill or be killed. It was as simple as that. But not the Yanks. This was news to them. Either that or their infantrymen and ours were distinctly dissimilar. For why would they be coming to us to supply them with pistols to send home. Couldn't their own "combat men" get those coveted prize enemy pistols for them?

Apparently not, for they persistently came round our encampments when we were getting our break from the Line and were resting up. And they would tout openly for those German pistols from our lads and were prepared to pay lots of dollars for them because they were allowed to send them home to the States. And they were readily accommodated, you can bet your bottom dollar on that. There would be hurried searches through British kit bags and packs to find those precious weapons for our rich allies.

And it wouldn't tax the brain-box too much to guess how those sales pitches would have went. Yankee soldier to H.L.I. soldier. "Say, Bud, how much for that Lugar you got there?" H.L.I. soldier to Yankee soldier "Which one . . .? Oh you mean that one! Give you it for five dollars." Yank to H.L.I. soldier "Sold. You got yourself a deal, boy. And I'll take a Mauser too if you can lay your hands on one."

It was incomprehensible to us all why the Yanks wanted those German weapons. In the first place although we all broke the rules at times it was still a court martial offence to withhold enemy weapons. And anyway why on earth would Chuck or Wilbur Jnr want to send a a German pistol home to mom and dad? The Five Star Generals got round the subject by saying that the G.I.s were only allowed to send one gun home at a time and then only as souvenirs.

Another story doing the rounds especially in Normandy was that the G.I.s sent the occasional pistol home as proof to let everyone know how they had actually tackled a nasty Nazi at close range. Not only that, but it was whispered to us that they would on occasions enclose a note stating that not content with taking that nasty German prisoner, but that they had given him a damned good old fashioned Yankee hiding before taking that damned elusive pistol from him. That would surely make them a hero in that old home town of theirs in the U.S. of A. It was the stuff films were made of. Yes Siree!

To be fair this latter statement had never actually been confirmed by anyone much as many of us would have liked it to have been. Because to be perfectly honest, it could well have sprung from the fact that despite being our Allies the Yanks got up most if not everyone's nose. And why? Simply because they were so bloody stupid most of the time. And not just their Private soldiers. Their corporals, their sergeants also with their upside down stripes, and most of their generals too with their ridiculous row of medals reaching from their chest down to their navels." Amateurs undoubtedly." That was a quote from the greatest general of them all, the one and only Monty.

For it was well known that Field Marshall Montgomery had had endless battles with their Top Brass and that included General Eisenhower. And it was all about the American tactics and some of their infantile rules and regulations, like fining a soldier 500 dollars for not wearing his tin hat when he should have, even when that soldier may well have been having a crap at the time. Then inexplicably permitting their G.Is to buy German weapons from their British soldier counterparts, and even worse, allowing them to send them home to America.

Whilst it would be churlish to suggest that we ourselves didn't make any mistakes, and bearing in mind that old adage about "The man who never made a mistake never made anything." It was also true that the Yanks had made some horrendous blunders before D Day. Before Dunkirk even. And whilst admitting that we didn't exactly come out of the Dunkirk thing covered in glory and tried to turn a humiliating defeat into a "strategic withdrawal," the fact still remained that the Americans had succeeded in turning training blunders into an Art Form.

They were blowing up their own men down in Devon during exercises shortly after they'd come over to Britain in a blaze of glory and not just once. It had almost becoming part of their training it seems. Blunders galore. Those Americans could go on at length about Buffalo Bill. But don't ever mention Portland Bill to some of their so-called Top Sailors. It's said that some Devon folk will never forget those American naval training disasters that were perpetrated on them in the early days of the 1940s. Nor will they ever forgive them for it.

But it was all hushed up, because the British Army was so pleased they had joined our side that they decided to close their eyes and ears to it all.

Simply because of the endless supply of money and material and so-called "know how" the Yanks brought for us to help beat the Germans. In fact there was another story doing the rounds then especially after all those home made disasters of theirs. And those cynics (some may say, wise men) said that if the Yanks had just given us the material and let their men join the other side we would have beaten the Germans a lot earlier.

Even Monty they reckon, had been known to admit that whereas he had done his military training at Sandhurst and other military colleges, most of the American generals had served their military apprenticeships in Hollywood and Broadway. The truth was they had perfected mediocrity. And had medals on their chests to prove it. But that wasn't all, not by any means. There was that other little matter that happened in Northern France and which the world read about, including the Germans too I shouldn't wonder.

Flying flags at full mast and pitching tents in full view of the enemy in the Ardennes while the rest of us were out enjoying a well earned rest after a magnificent break-through were only some of the things the daft Yanks had got up to. Then, after they all had got well and truly drunk, they started celebrating prematurely by firing off flares and cavorting about with the local talent. And in so doing had unwittingly but stupidly pin-pointed out all our positions to the Germans, who promptly upped, counter-attacked and over-ran them literally catching them with their trousers down. Thus throwing the whole allied advance into chaos. Needless to say all this didn't endear us to them or them to us come to that.

In fact it was Smithy who seized the opportunity to have another go at them. It was common knowledge that he couldn't stand the Yanks at any price. Now that they'd dropped us in the shit once more and we would have to go back from our break to try and regain the territory that they had lost us due to their childish stupidity he really went to town about them with even more vehemence than usual.

But to be fair most of our anger stemmed from sheer envy at what they had and what we had not. OK so they were our Allies. We should have been more tolerant of them. But what do you do when you're standing in a bar in London or somewhere else nursing a half-pint of beer and see those Yanks buying all the civvies a drink then shagging all their own women and some of ours as well.

Ask any British soldier and he would tell you the same story. Not only that but we then had to listen to them telling everyone how they and they alone along with General Bloody-Guts Patton of course were going to beat the Germans and win the war for all of us! "Let me tell you guys. He's one helluva general," one heavily tanned superfinely-serged corporal told us once. I mean a body could only take so much.

That was one of the reasons why poor old Smithy had a go at them. "Why doesn't one of your own fucking "C" men get you a German Lugar?" he told one of them shortly before the Ardennes fiasco when they came round to our camp one day to buy pistols to send home. And he completely lost the head with one of them. To the uninitiated, a Yankee soldier sporting a large "C" on his sleeve then was supposed to let the outside world know but curiously enough not to us for some time, that those Yankee soldiers were the equivalent of our infantrymen.

And we didn't know. And why didn't we know? Maybe, just maybe, it was because we hadn't seen many of them around. Apart that is from those other common or garden American "C"s we'd all seen buying everyone drinks in all the pubs. But now we did know that a guy sporting that large "C" on his arm was a "Combat Man" no less. And all this had obviously brought something all back to Smithy and myself which had happened to us in Aldershot whilst preparing for D Day. Then it wasn't motivated by anger but it was nonetheless memorable for all that.

Our commanding officer at the time had obviously made a decision one night over a glass of wine with his American opposite number we surmised. "What a spiffing idea," he probably said it would be if some of his chaps could come and share a billet for a night with their American counterparts, just to see how the other half lived so to speak and to get to know them. And so the deal was done. It would all be a first rate public relations exercise. Get To Know Your Ally sort of stuff; what what! It should be stressed however that this was to be non-reciprocal. I mean, it had to be. Hadn't it?

Because even our top-drawer C.O. wasn't that dim. I mean, who could see the Yanks facing rissoles and haricot beans for breakfast with watery tea and dried milk as an extra. Anyway two men were chosen from each platoon for "The Experiment". Smithy and I were chosen to represent our lot. And you can talk all you like about getting one's eyes opened. Smithy and I had ours literally prised open and they remained open for the whole twenty-four hours we were there.

True it was a common or garden Nissen hut that the American Artillery whose guests we were to be for the next twenty fours were billetted in but there the similarity ended.

The interior was chocolate box stuff. First there were individual beds to start with. I never knew single beds existed in the army except in the officers quarters. And the hut was beautifully painted with nursery rhymes on the wall and quotations from famous Americans headlining their names after each quote.

At this, needless to say, Smithy sarcastically said to me he didn't think there was any famous Americans. I shook my head at him. Then he asked me to prove him wrong by naming one. And for the life of me I just couldn't recall a single one apart maybe from W.C. Fields. It was probably unfair, because even by the law of averages, surely there just had to be at least one.

Fluorescent lighting replaced the single 50 watt rubbishy bulbs we had, something else we had never ever seen before especially in a Nissen hut. Extra blankets and feather pillows were also piled neatly beside each bed alongside a bedside lamp. "Do they supply women too I wonder?" asked Smithy sarcastically. "I wouldn't be surprised if they did," I replied. But truly we were both overcome at the splendour we were seeing in the middle of war time.

They also had hangers for their superfine serge uniforms. Again something only afforded our officers. "And we're not even allowed to wear a fucking tie yet," hissed Smithy as he felt the texture of a tunic that was hanging there. Smithy and I slept so well that night we could have sworn that both of us had been anaesthetised beforehand. Those feather pillows certainly worked wonders for us.

But it was the next morning at breakfast that made our eyes stick out like organ stops when we lined up alongside other G.Is for what they called "the Breakie Walk." There we were handed a tray by an orderly who was black with a set of pearly white teeth which accentuated his blackness but didn't stop him grinning probably at our open mouths. We proceeded down the "Walk" with our trays with those four intriguing indentations on them for those goodies we could see and as we moved down along the line we were asked our preference for either orange juice or apple juice. We were then asked if we preferred our eggs scrambled or fried, and if fried did we want our eggs fried over easy or not? Neither Smithy nor myself knew what the black chef with the white hat meant so we decided to seize the moment before it was gone for ever. "We don't mind how they come mate so long as they're eggs," said Smithy grinning all over his face. "And how do you like your bacon gentlemen? Crispy or soft? Or would you prefer cereal or maybe porridge?"

We were both dumbstruck. The only time I had ever ever seen so much food, was at weddings or on screen at the pictures. Even the butter was separated from the toast.

That meant you could spread it on yourself as much as you liked. I had to literally kick Smithy to keep him moving along the line, simply because he was holding everyone up. His mouth was open wide, drooling. You could have driven a double- decker bus straight through it.

Then came the pièce de résistance, the coffee which I must say came as a complete surprise to me. I had always thought that all coffee was black and came out of a kind of H.P. sauce bottle and it was called Camp Coffee, and it had to be drunk in Lyons Corner shop in London. Even then it was said that it was for officers only. But this coffee was pure yellow and there was no notice to say "Officers Only". Just gallons of steaming yellow creamy coffee full to the brim in stainless steel pails just begging to be scoffed. There wasn't one tea urn in sight.

A slightly dazed Smithy and myself ate and drank yellow coffee till we could hardly move. Even closing our mouths was an effort. It had all been a little too much for both of us. The rest of the squad would never believe us if we ever managed to scramble to our feet to get back to tell them. Just before we said our goodbyes the big black orderly who had attended to our every whim wished us luck.

Then just as we were going out the door with our kit packed all ready to return back to arseholes, rissoles, haricot beans and reality, a well honed American corporal approached us. "Did you guys enjoy your stay?" We both nodded our gratitude. He then pointed to a poster up on the wall. It depicted a G.I. in action It was an all action shot of a G.I. At the Ready, no less!

"Good. Glad you enjoyed it," he grinned. "The grub could have been better though. But let me say this," he hissed clenching his fist and pointing to the caption on the wall. "We don't mind going a bit short of food as long as those guys are getting it!" Smithy and I followed his pointing finger to the Action Man depicted on the wall. What was that on Action Man's right sleeve? Look closer. Yes. You guessed right.

There it was for all the world to see. A very large "C" . . . We regaled the platoon when we got back about the grub and the other luxuries we'd had with the Yanks. They all stood open-mouthed as we told them about getting two eggs for breakfast every morning instead of getting one egg for breakfast every six weeks or so. At first they refused to believe us. "Two eggs at one sitting? Jammy bastards," was one incredulous comment. Then when we went on about the pails of yellow coffee that were on offer we were almost shouted down.

We then told them about the posters we had seen on the walls of the Yankee Combat Men. Or to give them their proper name, the "C" men. There were howls of laughter at this, mostly directed at Smithy. "You should have told them you were even better than that. That you were an "F 'n C" man, Smithy. And they wouldn't have been far wrong believe you me," shouted Pricey derisively at a somewhat flummoxed Smithy.

Despite all that generosity afforded us by the Americans I honestly believed that Smithy hated the Yanks even more than that postman who was knocking about with his wife back in Birmingham. And in fact from what I'd gathered Smithy's domestic troubles had been on-going since the two years or so I'd known him. He didn't discuss the matter much. But Smithy's love life was one of our platoon's worst kept secrets. And this was more the fault of Smithy himself rather than any of us, as he would often swear openly to put a certain postman in such a position that he would never be able to post or deliver another letter again. There was also a whisper doing the rounds too about a Yank hovering and sniffing in the background. This could also account for Smithy's love of the Allies! . . .

Any time Smithy went on a 48-hour leave he never came back in 48 hours. In fact more often than not M.P.s had to be sent to Birmingham to escort him back to barracks. And return he would with bruises to prove it. And you could bet they were not inflicted by his wife or even by that postman. It was well known that Smithy had a vile temper. So too did some of those M.P's, for Smithy was no slouch at the punching game. One against one that is . . .

But he was a good soldier. A fact that did not go unnoticed in higher echelons. All this despite his at times lengthy stays in the guard room. In fact there was a standing story not put about by me I can assure you. And the story went something like this. "Anybody seen Smithy?" "No. Isn't he in the guard room?" "No, he's not." "Then he must be on leave again." Poor Smithy. But Smithy was alright by me. And I was alright by him. And he proved them all wrong in Holland, and no doubt he was still doing alright wherever he was . . .

Pricey on the other hand was a different kettle of fish entirely. No domestic trouble there. And you got the impression he intended to keep it that way. Because ever since he joined us from the Vickers machine gun pool in 1942 round about the same time as Smithy and myself he didn't wait to be confined to barracks. Pricey confined himself to barracks. He seldom if ever went out dancing, to the pictures or anywhere else for that matter.

"On you go. Don't worry about me," he would say to Smithy and I whenever pay day came along and we would invite him along. "I'm just going to lie here in my kip and write a couple of letters." Then just as we would be about to exit our hut hastily as most of us were wont to do in those drab days when we were all being specially brought in to form a special unit of Vickers Machine Gunners, he would cry out teasingly, "Oh and by the way try and behave yourselves."

It wasn't that he was reclusive or anything like that. True he was a little older than Smithy and I but he mucked in just like the rest of us, no lectures or any of that rubbish despite that slight disparity in ages. But one thing was certain. He was officer material. There was no question about that. He was tall, bordering on the six foot mark with slightly balding gingerish hair and a certain dedication that to be honest was lacking in the rest of us. We also knew that he was a trainee school teacher, and was keen to become the real thing when the war ended. He also came from Manchester. "Don't worry about it mate. Somebody's got to come from Manchester," I remember Smithy telling him jokingly when he first joined us.

One thing was for sure however. What Smithy was, Pricey was not. And if it was going to take writing letters every night to keep his sweetheart and his love life alive then it would be letters every night that God sent to whoever that girl may be. For that's the kind of guy Pricey was. Or to give him his full name, James Alan Price. Like I said his application hadn't entirely gone un-noticed. For he was only with us a few weeks before he was made up to acting lance corporal. Nor was there even the slightest trace of sour grapes from any of us about his swift promotion. Not even from the most envious in that platoon of ours.

" You'd think he'd take one night off from writing bloody letters home wouldn't you?" Here we go again, I used to say to myself when Smithy and I used to go out for a night to the village pub to see what we could scrounge or to see if our sexual magnetism was still endemic among the local females.

Because although the affair between Smithy's wife and that postman still rankled, Smithy was a Deacon of Double Standards. All women were there for the taking except of course, Smithy's. And he had no problem with the ethics of that. But as an unattached person myself I could speak with a certain amount of objectivity and actually told him that he should take a leaf out of Pricey's book, and send off the occasional missive to his wife Glynis. That way I reckoned our rogue postman would then have had to restrict himself to delivering letters instead of the "collection" side of the game.

And indeed I spoke to him often about it over and over again, trying to be objective about the whole thing. I even suggested that he should phone her daily despite all the difficulties of getting near a telephone in those austere days. And he actually did phone her; once. He almost bit my head off for even suggesting he kept it up "Me? Why should I? Did you know the bastard's a Conchie?" It was only some time later that he confessed to me that he meant to say that it was the postman who was the conscientious objector, not his wife. And many a time since I've often pondered as to who exactly was the real culprit in the Smithy Domestic Drama. The Adulteress Wife. Or that Conscientious Objector of a Postman!!

But despite all his shortcomings there was not a lot wrong with our Smithy. Not the ideal husband maybe. And somewhat lacking in know-how in the marital stakes and naive possibly but as genuine as they came. And fiercely proud of his Brummie roots. I wouldn't mind betting that he, Pricey and young Sonny would be keeping the flag flying in Germany or whatever spot they happened to be in when that bloody war came to an end. Even now I could see him behind the wheel of that carrier driving in his usual cavalier fashion flicking that straight scruffy blonde hair of his away from his eyes and defying anyone to beat him to wherever the hell they were going. Deep down, despite the depression within me I wanted desperately to be there with them . . .

The war in Europe was only over a few months and there was I along with some other lucky ones heading for Germany the easy way - tourist style by train, and a proper boat sort of. That's if you considered what we'd crossed the water in to the Hook of Holland was a proper boat. Notwithstanding it was still comparative luxury compared to the way Smithy and company would be travelling. It would be blood, sweat and tears there and no mistake. I just hoped and prayed that they had all managed to keep their heads down until that final whistle sounded. The buggers might even be back in old Blighty. It was a distinct possibility. And it would just be like the thing if they were all already back home safe and sound. I would need to start getting some information soon about them and the unit in general.

Then the confirmation that Smithy, Pricey and Sonny were all OK was dropped into my lap right out of the blue! Even when I was reading it with my very own eyes it was still a shock. But a very pleasant shock indeed. Not back home maybe. But they were safe! I couldn't believe it at first. They were safe and sound, all three of them. Maybe not back home yet. But they were alive somewhere. And their names for once didn't flash in front of my eyes like one's life is supposed to when one is dying. Exactly the reverse was true.

It all came about just when our train was about to pull out of Hamburg. Our train had only literally moved a few inches when another troop train was shunted in alongside us on the next platform. We were then halted abruptly on a signal. Something was obviously afoot.

The officer in charge of us then lowered his window and spoke to another British officer on the other train. He then withdrew, and told the sergeant entrusted to our squad. "Hold on. There may well be a delay. The men can stand down momentarily until further orders. I shouldn't be too long. Half an hour should do it." The sergeant saluted him and we watched from our windows as off he went along the platform up the steps and across the bridge to the train on the other side. It was obvious to us all that a meeting had been hastily convened. What we called an "O" Group. The Military name for a chin-wag.

We de-trained and were told to stand easy. Cigarettes were produced and smoking commenced once more amongst us. Guilt began to show on faces now that they knew what that "Achtung" sign which was frowning down on them, meant. That half hour became an hour before our officer re-appeared, this time with a sheaf of papers peeping out from a large brown folder which he carried under his left arm. We were then ordered back on train. Something was wrong. The sergeant was called to the officer's compartment almost immediately. The train then pulled out of Hamburg's station one hour and a half later than scheduled!

One hour later we stopped again. This time it was an emergency stop. Our only officer had been taken ill. Appendicitis had been diagnosed by a civilian doctor who had been taken aboard at Hamburg. The patient would have to be hospitalised back in Hamburg. Time was of the essence seemingly when an appendix burst. The sergeant would escort him there then for some reason best known to himself I was ordered into the officer's compartment to keep an eye on things. There was no time to spare and anyway who was I to argue with a sergeant? Not only that but there was a lot more room in there. Big enough even to have a lie down in I remember thinking. "Just sit in there till I get back," he said, and with that he was gone. I felt somewhat uneasy. My head was going back to Overloon, and I couldn't prevent all that throbbing . . .

A pile of forms lay on the seat in the compartment. They weren't marked Top Secret or Censored or anything like that. However there was one bulky file also there, marked "Not For Public Scrutiny". That was when curiosity took over. Quick as a flash I flicked over the top page. And there was the caption. Overlord. 1944 Europe. Theatres Of War. I then turned the second page over. And there in bold capitals were three headings. *FRANCE. BELGIUM. HOLLAND.* And below each country there was a name, number, and rank.

I shut the file immediately and sat down. A feeling of guilt began to course through me. My heart and head were pounding. This was not for me, I shouldn't be doing this sort of thing. I was in a bad enough state as it was. Why was I in here looking at files of dead men when I myself was sitting there safe, if not quite sound!

Vividly, I remember closing my eyes for fully ten minutes, with my heartbeat almost outstripping the purring noise of the train as it sped through the green fields of Germany. I also remember hoping against hope that the sergeant, anyone at all for that matter, would come bursting through that door to release me from the turmoil within me. But no one ever did come through that door . . . ! No one. No one . . .

I sat as long as I could trying to convince myself that I was doing no good by not looking at those names in that file. Because either way I knew it could be bad news. Or it could be nothing at all. So I steeled myself as best as I could and gradually got better with practice, at calming myself down, practice, practice, I kept repeating to myself over and over again then stood up as resolutely as I possibly could despite the vacuous feeling in my head again and began to turn over those pages of those names and numbers with trembling fingers . . .

So tremulous in fact that I had to try to coax some saliva from my mouth to the tips of my fingers to help me do just that. I half closed my eyes at the endless rows of names and numbers that leapt out out at me, pages and pages of the stuff. They were neverending. Three columns for each country. *FRANCE. DEAD. MISSING. PRESUMED DEAD. WOUNDED* Names . . . ! Names . . . ! Hundreds of them! Fortunately there were none that were known to me. But then that was bloody war for you. And anyway we had all managed through that bloody French minefield, thank you very much. My trembling fingers lingered over Belgium . . . "John Smith. Private," was one name that caught my eye. Plenty of those too. Right Name. Wrong country. We had all fought our way through there too. So it wouldn't be there either. So there was just one more country to go. But it was the one that mattered. It was the country where everything fell apart for our lot, *HOLLAND*. My digit finger moved along an unending list of names. My finger dallied over the category, *DEAD*. And there were no names there that I knew and I thanked God again. Funny how your head kept telling you things as you looked at things that didn't always add up . . .

Then over to the *MISSING PRESUMED DEAD*. Again I dallied deliberately. For often that held the key. If your name was there, it could mean anything. It could mean being stuck in a P.O.W. camp somewhere, sick perhaps even dying. but not yet found. It could mean anything. It could also mean that you could be running around bomb-happy, not knowing where you were or even what you were, like myself. But the main thing was, my name wasn't there. Nor were any of the others, Smithy, Pricey or Sonny. And that's what mattered.

They could call me what they liked. But my mates were neither dead nor missing, and that would do for me. So it was with a lighter heart that I then scoured the *WOUNDED* list and found no names there. I breathed a sigh of relief and hastily closed those files. Then I began wondering to myself. Who made up those lists of the Dead, the Wounded and the Missing Presumed Dead. It was all so impersonal I thought. Like some latter day made-up God compiling his list of those he'd chosen to go with him into Paradise. And there was I being every bit as presumptuous as anyone doing my Peeping Tom Act on the *DEAD*, the *MISSING PRESUMED DEAD* and the *WOUNDED*. Still I gritted my teeth and read on. I well knew I was no Master Spy. And it may well have been an attempt at aggrandisement on my part even. Something, to make me feel a bit better by knowing that they were all alive and kicking. People could then brand me with whatever name they like. I had stopped caring, but please God, just let those lists be true . . .

After perusing those lists I felt I knew how those people who I used to see at the pictures felt when Pathetone News showed pictures of women and children waiting and praying at pitheads for news of their loved ones trapped down below. It was no worse than that. But then again it was no better. I was momentarily tempted to flick through those lists just to make sure, but resisted the temptation, lay back and closed my eyes and was glad that I had done the right thing.

And who knows I may yet run across them in the Germany I was making for! . . . My head wasn't telling me any anything more. Or was it my eyes?...

## Chapter Five

*Deliverance Day Plus One*

Our lot went over to Normandy on D plus one. Not you'll notice on D Day itself. The reason for that was simple; we just weren't ready. Everyone else may have been ready and had sailed off into the sunset on the 6th June 1944. But our wee boat wasn't keeping enough water out. Instead it was keeping it in when it shouldn't have, so more *Bostik* was called for. *Bostik* was a sealing substance, which was supposed to be the solution for everything around Aldershot in those hush-hush-days. There were also niggling doubts about our boat's capabilities. That being so, we were all poised for an extra night on the town. But alas it did not materialise. All leave was cancelled at the last minute. Our rations were cut to get us used to doing with little or no food. There were some that would say we already had been so trained for the past four years.

Training was intensified and rations austere; that meant that all we had to live on for the first week or so was tea and wads. This meant a dash from *Bostik*ing up on or around the barrack square to the Naafi and to try to get served in the fifteen minutes break-time allotted to us. In fact our sole solace was to sup tea and munch wads quickly and group round the one solitary billiard table that was in the canteen. But we made the most of that fifteen-minute break make no mistake about that.

But no matter how hard we all tried we invariably found that the table was once more engaged as ever by the same two squaddies. "Employed men," so called because they did only "light duties". These usually consisted of men who were either awaiting their "ticket" for some reason or other. Maybe they had suddenly developed flat feet or something. Or were just not fighting fit. Were indeed any of us for that matter, we would often ask ourselves.

Mainly, our "spare pair" would be employed as full-time latrine wallahs. This more or less meant that they were their own boss and could take their breaks whenever they liked and they seemed to take them when the main squads were wanting a game on the table. And by the very nature of there "being lying handy", were always first in line in the grub queue also. Predictably they were dubbed "Shit" by all and sundry for that was what they dealt with day in day out. It's what they did best. I don't think anyone knew their real names.

So the only luxury afforded to most of us was to sit round and watch the cue actions of our ubiquitous denim-clad pair as they plied their undoubted talents on that green plush surface. and to applaud unstintingly where appropriate. The rafters would often reverberate to wry whistles and caustic cries of,

"Bloody good shot there, Shit." And often the more perfunctory but nonetheless derisory, "Shot Shit. Bloody good shot, Shit!" "Excellent play there, Shit!"

But this seldom if ever embarrassed our table toppers. They had got used to it. Ironically, if anyone, who wasn't a cook-house wallah or a shit-house wallah, and was restricted by such insignificant items, like preparing to invade another country such as France you were bang in trouble. Because if you wanted a game on that table you were requested to put your name in the book and wait your turn. So Smithy and I did just that and by a simple process of counting the number of troops in and around Aldershot at that time and taking away the number you first thought of sort of thing, we reckoned we could easily qualify for a game round about 1976. So we decided not to bother.

Frustration dwelt most certainly within us all. It was the night before tomorrow as that old saying went and there we were getting settled in our bunks hoping to make the next day, our last day, a memorable one before going overseas, when those dreaded words; "All troops confined to barracks" hit us over the tannoy. It was made even harder to take since we had all sworn to drink Aldershot dry and to reduce the virginity rate amongst the local talent significantly. That was something else we would never achieve for yesterday's events in Normandy were overshadowing all else.

The news was that the first landing hadn't gone all that well. Intelligence reports had stated that resistance to the landings had been more fierce than was first anticipated. This was an all too familiar Secret Service euphemism for heavy losses being incurred. The news dampened our ardour somewhat and the desires of the flesh too and brought us suddenly back to earth. We felt for the lads who had gone that one day before us to their untimely deaths. For that's what it meant no matter in what contrived words that intelligence message was couched. We were put on Full Alert. It would be an early "Lights Out" for us all, and to sleep the uneasy sleep . . . !

When dawn came we sailed away from Tilbury. Those who had dreamed up the idea of tanks and Bren carriers floating on what were little more than reinforced dinghys we hoped had got it right and in the main they had. So across the channel we went and our particular carrier almost made it to the beach itself but not quite. To be fair, we were warned about that possibility. So it was a case of wading ashore with rifles held high and to swim if you could, to get feet on that dry land, and obey that last order to "Engage". "Engage." Again only if you could. But we couldn't. Resistance was there in abundance. Whizzing, whining shrapnel waited there to puncture and rip your quivering body wide open if you'd let it!

We shouted and shouted ourselves ashore as prescribed in the drill to ease the tension and climbed a slight incline in the sands to see what we could see despite the constant hum of mortar bombs and eighty-eighties cascading all around us. Get those shovels out. Get digging fast and get down from that hellfire surface or get your head chopped from you. That was the choice. One shovel between two. One each may have been better. But it didn't run to that.

Lucky Yanks had one each. Smaller certainly but one each. Something about extra baggage prevented us being as fortunate. Two to a slit, one lying flat whilst the other dug, taking turns to get on with it, for getting down quickly was the thing, the only thing. Even when you managed to get your head beneath that mortar-scorched surface your immediate instinct was to try and burrow your head still further and further into that earth and eat worms just to get away from it all.

Because the fear of dying was upon you and you fought to survive. Please God, give me another day! And at the risk of tempting fate dear God, perhaps a little longer. For only someone who had been there and had actually dug down deep enough to live, could describe the feeling of relief that enveloped you when you eventually did manage to get under. For there you would sit with your head between your knees. You at one end of that hastily dug slit trench and your mate at the other end, shouting and shouting to drown out the moans of those dying around you.

Then the test, to lift your head to see if you were still alive despite the constant pounding on the earth above and the constant thumping in your eardrums. And scream; yes scream. Scream your screams and scream your songs at each other as loud as your lungs would allow. Scream your obscenities, but whisper your prayers just in case. It was all to do with releasing the tension within you someone had told us so that you might not go mad, that you might even live. I managed to inch my head above the trench. For one whole solid hour they'd managed to pin us down and it wasn't just my watch that was telling me. It was the tremor that was almost possessing me, a feeling that you tried to fight with every fibre of your being. It was something you had to fight to keep down, something you had to keep under control.

It was then I saw him and I was tempted to forsake all as I spotted an army chaplain midst all that carnage of burning tanks and vehicles. He could only be a Catholic priest with his scapular around his neck, he was striding on seemingly oblivious of the hell and stuff that was bombarding us all. I observed him from my own slit trench striding further and further on with only our artillery for back up. More men then began to dart from their holes to try to catch up with this fearless, mystery man of God in an effort to unburden themselves and to seek absolution for their sins and to save themselves from hell. " What Hell?" I kept asking myself. Were their varying degrees of it? Like burns? Or was this not hell where we were at this moment?

I watched even as the Stukas dived for us and saw some of my own outfit catching up with the priest, trotting alongside him, being heard, being blessed then dropping out to be replaced by another in some grotesque confessional relay. And the better for it or not? Who was to say? Was it worth getting your head chopped off by a mortar? Or halved in two by an eighty-eight millimetre shell? Debatable. It may well have been all of those things, but I was having myself a basinful. Because to me, this was Jesus, walking. And suddenly I wanted to be alongside him and have me some "See you later, sonny". I shouted and jumped out to take my chance in the race for God . . .

"Say one for me when you're over there, you windy bastard" shouted Smithy. But I wasn't listening to him or anybody else for that matter. He could call me what he liked. To Smithy all religions were nothing but a load of "bollocks". His words not mine. Smithy was entitled to his opinion. But I was listening to my conscience. And I had made my mind up to do something about it. Despite laying himself open to being chopped to pieces at any moment that priest continued to dispense absolution individually by kissing the scapular after each hearing. And by this very action he was offering privacy to the confessors on those hellish Normandy sands. In spite of the crescendo of shells, more and more men were vacating their trenches and joining him to be heard and to receive absolution from what to me, was a very brave man.

And even the fear of instant death by leaving their hole in the ground, arguably the only safe place on those shell-ridden sands just to be able to unload, or even to be able to talk to someone made rubbish of those traditional denominational divisions. And that's why C of Es, Presbyterians and Jews, must all have seen the advantage of at least being able to cope with the Limbo we were all in that day. For this was no time for segregation!

For me, this was a time to accept that Jesus was actually walking and listening in Normandy whether in the guise of a priest or a rabbi or a Presbyterian minister for that matter. I had missed going to confession in Aldershot before embarking on the great adventure. That gave me the impetus to just do what I did. So there and then I made a tryst with my God to get me out of it alive and safe. And in return I would never miss going to Mass ever again as long as I lived. I sincerely hoped he was listening and would believe me.

Then a hush, a cessation of those deadly eighty-eights and those murderous mortars. Breathe in and out as evenly as you could. For it may be just a pause, a ruse. But no; maybe they were just running out of men? Or it could just be a role reversal and suddenly you just knew that's what it was. And it was our turn. It was then that our very own armada out there in the channel began to hit back with the big stuff. Noisier certainly but they were our very own. Our artillery too were now making their presence felt, getting in on the act and for once the music was sweet!

I shouted over once more to Sonny whom I'd been shouting across at and he to me for the past hour or so. Sonny; that's what we called him. He was my oppo in the hole opposite. He of the almost unpronounceable surname, Soninka, I think it was. He was of Lithuanian descent and his little round face was forever smiling. I should have sent him over to the priest too. Surely he wasn't C of E with a name life Soninka. Although you couldn't tell these days. For some reason we all dodged his surname, so he was Sonny to us all and a more apt nickname would be difficult to find anywhere.

He was our new Number Two gunner and had only joined us a few days ago in Aldershot. He was whole and he was alive and I was whole and I was alive too. And we shouted over to that other hole and discovered to our joy that Pricey and Smithy were also OK. We were all alive and kicking, thank God. We then lay back in our holes and waited with not a little trepidation, the command to advance. "It's alright for some," shouted Smithy over to me. A reference to my dart over for confession no doubt.

The command came so we mounted carriers and moved forward in the direction of Caen, which we were told was only a few kilometres further on. Intelligence reports said that there had been fierce fighting in and around that historic Norman town, and there had been heavy casualties on both sides. Hence the plastering we had to endure as the Germans fought to regain a little momentum. As we progressed what had happened twenty-four hours earlier began to unfold slowly in front of our very eyes. As the pall of smoke from the shells abated a bit we were to see at first hand the brutal reality of it all. The sweet sickly odour of hastily interred bodies began to play on one's nostrils. There was no escaping it.

Close your eyes and you still saw those little mounds of earth representing a grave. A crudely shaped wooden cross with a gashed helmet perched precariously and grotesquely on top would tell you if that little pile covering parts of a body, was British or American, or even German. It was then I noticed something after looking at those gashed helmets that marked those graves. Something didn't quite add up.

For every one British helmet fluttering in what little breeze there was, were two American helmets. Was this coincidence? I wondered. Were our helmets really stronger than theirs? Were their soldiers twice as brave as ours? Had they in fact put twice as many more men into the fray as we had? Somehow I doubted that. Then it struck me. It was the shovels. It was those bloody shovels of theirs, those collapsible neat little shovels the Americans carried strapped to their webbing and envied by us for their lightness. Collapsible sadly being the operative word here I thought. Those poor buggers weren't able to get dug into their slit trenches fast enough when the Germans were hitting us with all those mortars and eighty-eights! . . .

That just had to be the solution I thought. We may only have had one shovel between two of us but they were *real* shovels. And they got you under a lot quicker that those poor Yanks who had been saddled with what I could only describe as pieces of metal resembling a child's spade. And what was the result? Those toys, for that's what they were, were only capable of scraping the surface and not fit for real purposeful digging. Those men just wouldn't get under in time. Their shovels may have been ideal for digging sand-castles that was about all. They were most certainly not made to get their soldier under and temporarily away from those perpetual eighty-eights and mortar bombs that would rain mercilessly down on them as they frantically fought to dig in. It was a grave error, and a costly one for those Americans who just couldn't get below ground in time.

I wondered what Smithy would say to that. It might make him ease up a bit on the Yanks, but somehow I doubted it. It was just one more American blunder. Safety had been sacrificed for fashion, in my opinion. I may be wrong, but I stand by my convictions. And I promised myself never to criticise our own common or garden shovels ever again, even if we didn't have one apiece. Someone should pay for what I considered to be a faulty design on that Yankee shovel. And that ratio of two American helmets to one British helmet would bear testimony to that.

Another unglamorous statistic that possibly didn't warrant the attention that it should have was the fact that each one of those little graves would remain shallow, just marginally below ground until the arrival of those greatly under-rated Royal Pioneer Corps following on behind. For theirs was the task of ensuring that each and every one of those men were re-interred decently and with some semblance of dignity to be visited at a later date all ready for wreaths to be laid on them. For that was the drill. That was the way it was done. That was the way it had to be done.

A burnt-out Sherman tank lay on its side still smouldering with no sign of life from within. The turret lay alongside. Bren carriers just like our own lay there too halted dead in their tracks by something bigger and greater or better positioned than we were. All those factors contributed in some way to those shallow graves and a frightening number of them there were. The Big Shots had got their numbers wrong once again for there were far more deaths than the amount predicted. If ever there was a right amount that is . . .

We tried to blot it all out as we progressed through the rich pasturelands of Normandy. The wounded were being ferried back aboard small ships, big ships, and in fact any craft that was seaworthy at all was being commandeered to get the severely wounded home across the channel. Regimental Aid posts were also being quickly erected. Everywhere you looked urgency was the order of the day. Get the dead buried and get the wounded out. Get them walking if they could but get them out at all cost. Yet despite all the sombre scenes that surrounded us, our troops, especially those that had gone that twenty-four hours before, had done their job well. They had made steady inroads towards their goal and that goal was the ancient city of Caen. Our task now was to consolidate those gains. So with infantry on either side of us and artillery behind us we pressed on, and made more headway still.

Our gunners traversed a long farmhouse with deadly 303s and succeeded in getting some prisoners to run out surrendering. It was heartening stuff we all felt. And how boyish they looked those troops. Seventeen? Eighteen? Could just as well have been sixteen. Hitler was surely scraping the bottom of the barrel. They looked scared to death. Little did they know we didn't feel any braver either. Not to show it was the trick. All part of the war game. Pricey, our Number One gunner, now acting Section Leader got off carrier, frisked them for concealed weapons, and grenades etc. then pointed them back to where some more had already been taken by our infantrymen. There they would be grouped for transportation, and possibly interrogated by Intelligence.

I couldn't speak for the others but deep down I felt things were beginning to go our way just a little. A kind of cautious optimism was beginning to take hold. It certainly helped settle my own nerves just a little and that had to be a plus. With a little bit of luck we might yet get out of all of this alive. I even detected a slight step up on our progress. But then just as suddenly those slight advances were halted and the digging-in began again. And they were always the worst were those abrupt halts. Because then you knew it just had to be the lightning stuff again with those sturdy shovels of ours just to keep alive. I thanked God for them once more. Dig. Dig. Dig, was the order of the day once more.

Each of us knew too that it would be time for reflection again just when you didn't want to reflect. Because you knew too that it would also be time for old fears to re-assert themselves within one and you didn't want that either. You wanted to press on and get it all over and done with. You also knew that it would mean that the enemy were very much on the qui vivre and would open up again with their terrifying heavy stuff. And it would be time once more for one of you to keep awake and be alert in order to stay alive while the other slept or tried to sleep through the turmoil of it all.

And of course that's what it was for the next few days, it was the stalemate thing then the digging-in thing on both sides again. The Germans were now taking full advantage of the situation. They knew through their own sources that we were still burying our dead. They also knew that our medics were desperately trying to transport the wounded all the way from the Caen area back to the ships to get them home so they mounted their own mini counter-attack. It could only be a limited attack our Intelligence reckoned. (And they should know shouldn't they?) Ha, bloody ha. For, according to them, the German army were already retreating from Caen and were heading north.

Whatever it was the German's heavy stuff lacked, their infantrymen and their small arms and machine guns more than made up for. After a short but nevertheless devastating spell with their "Moaning Minnies"; German mortars, so called because of the eerie moaning whining sound they made as they sped overhead, we were subjected to sporadic machine-gun fire. They were firing at us from some hedgerows about five hundred yards away and they had the added advantage of being quite a distance above us into the bargain.

Pricey and Number Two, young Sonny, responded well to my reading. As Number Two gunner, Sonny's job, was to feed the 303 ammunition belt through and to ensure that it was fed in straight otherwise the Vickers could jam. And then we would be in all sorts of trouble. Pricey often praised my range readings, saying that the Vickers no matter how accurate a weapon was only as good as the range it was given. And that always pleased me immensely. Not only did it make me feel good as indeed it did, but even better; it seemed to instil calmness within me and helped ease the nervous tension which continued to dog me. All this, and to know you were making a positive contribution to your fellow soldiers well being, would do for me.

With our artillery bombing above and in front of vast areas of hedgerows, we also made our mark with own brand of machine-gun fire Vickers style and continued to do so until their return fire finally ceased. And once more there was an upsurge of hope amongst us as we waited to see if our expectations were to be realized, and we had in fact, halted their comeback yet again. I hoped and prayed we had.

No matter how much I tried I just couldn't match the nonchalance of lance Jack Price or Smithy, or even newcomer Sonny. They appeared to take it all in their stride, especially Smithy. If he wasn't driving our carrier, and shouting at the same time he was in and out of those empty, sometimes burnt-out farmhouses, searching for loot with absolutely no thought for his own personal safety or for anyone else's come to that.

We had been warned and lectured at length about booby traps. But it didn't seem to worry Smithy one bit. Every time we were resting up or were bogged down due to roads being blocked by dead cattle or wrecked vehicles, he would be in there rooting around to see what he could scrounge. And for some reason or other he would want me to come with him on those somewhat precarious excursions of his.

One of his least brainy tactics was to pull open a drawer suddenly then hurl himself to the floor at the same time just in case it was booby-trapped. He did this on countless occasions even when I explained to him that he would hardly be travelling at the speed of sound and that he could be blown to smithereens long before he hit the floor. Although I did notice that he steered clear of drawers after that. When I was with him I always kept a fair distance behind, all this because of his renowned unpredictability...

I reckoned he was one of the most fearless persons I had ever come across and not just in the army. I mean anywhere. Foolhardy at times certainly but without any trace of fear. And I envied him for that. That was why I seldom refused when he asked me to explore those empty bombed-out, but tantalizingly tempting farmhouses outside Caen. But again I always kept my distance. Smithy was Smithy. I was me. That's how I saw it. Rightly or wrongly. Seldom did I ever try to dissuade him in anything. But there was one time when nothing was happening. No one was being shot at. And no one was being bombed. It was then that he and I fell out and all but came to blows over it.

The reason we were not being shot at or bombed was because we had been put on stand-by. A story doing the rounds was that the fall of Caen was imminent and judging by the sound our artillery and small arms fire were making the story had its merits. The moment we were informed that Caen had fallen our orders were to advance on the town, dig-in and hold. Most of us accepted what we'd been told; but not Smithy. He was just not prepared to hang about.

Maybe he was right, but as far I was concerned orders were orders. He had a very low boredom threshold did our Smithy. As if to make matters worse, Pricey had been called away for a special briefing and this made Smithy even more restless.

"We could be sitting around here for another two or three hours yet," he said. "Look at that farmhouse over there; it's never been touched. I'll bet there's loads of stuff in there just for the taking. How about it, some of you? Come on, let's see what we can get before it's all over." I shook my head. "Count me out Smithy. We could be moving off soon, and then what?"

He then directed his question to young Sonny. "How about you, Sonny boy." Sonny shrugged his shoulders. He was as bored as any of us, but despite being younger than any of us, he was a young man who behaved well, and had always acted responsibly. "I don't know. I don't think I should. We could be moving off any minute." It was sound sense from one so young.

"He's right, Smithy, and you know it," I said, "Pricey wouldn't have stood for it. So let's cut it out. Stay on the carrier. That's my suggestion. We should all stay here just in case." Of course there was nothing to prevent Smithy nicking off for as long as he liked provided he was prepared to take the consequences if we had suddenly to move off. Like I said, Pricey had been called away by our platoon commander for that briefing, and as far as I knew Smithy was the senior of the three of us. Not only that but he was the carrier driver and that alone was an enormous responsibility.

One thing was for sure, those dead cattle were presenting an enormous problem and not just to the advancing British army but to the French farmers in particular. Hundreds of dead cows, bulls and young calves, were strewn all over fields and ditches. Killed, not from any shrapnel, but from the mere blasts from those instruments of war. Even if those blasts occurred half a mile it had that same deadly effect on animals, we were told. It was one of those quirks of fate but a costly one for those French farmers.

Another problem created by the cattle was the manner of their dying. Whenever they were struck the animals would drop, then roll on to their backs and there they would stay with legs sticking grotesquely in the air. This then tended to make their bloated bellies swell even more, and putrifying the air to boot.

Not only that but the sheer bulk of those dead cattle were creating trouble on a monumental scale. The whole place was in danger of becoming one great bottleneck with hardly anything moving. Fields, roads and lanes were completely blocked with wrecked cars and burned-out tanks. Nothing, but nothing, was getting past. All this on an especially hot and sun-drenched blood-soaked day in Normandy. The French farmers were then joined by army officers and a hasty confab ensued. It was decided that it would be too time consuming to bury the cattle individually or even in twos. The problem was a huge one. There was no doubt about that.

Then once more it was the good old Pioneer Corps to the rescue. A decision was taken to bulldoze an area about the size of a football field and place the cattle in en masse and then incinerate the lot.

But before all this could take place, we were forced to sit and spectate at an even more sickening sight. The swollen bellies of the dead cows had to be deflated otherwise the hole huge as it was would never have been able to contain them all. Farmers had to take it in turn more or less to climb on to the animal's stomach. Then with a pickaxe and standing precariously astride the animal's stomach they had to try to puncture the animal's belly with the axe. This would thus enable the gases in the belly to be released and at the same time reduce the size of the animal. It was a slow, painful, and very unpleasant experience for everyone not least of all for those farmers.

I was no insurance expert but even to this day I often wondered if those farmers would ever be compensated for the loss of their cattle, not to mention suffering the indignity of having to put their cattle down in such a disgusting way. The Pioneers didn't have it all that easy either. They had the unenviable task of putting chains round the legs of the animals and dragging them down before releasing them into the hole which would eventually be their funeral pyre. And what of the Pioneer Corps? Our very own. There would most certainly be no compensation there. They were only doing their job. That's what the Big Shots, would say anyway.

But then that was war. Animals were being slaughtered but so too were our own brothers, they were being cut down as they landed from their skimpy little boats. So let's not dwell too long on the Cruelty to Animals thing. The wholesale disposal of those poor beasts certainly shook us all up. But there was one consolation at least. The spectacle of it all I prayed had put the idea of further looting from Smithy's mind at least for the time being.

I, for one, fervently hoped it had, because you didn't venture into those empty and sometimes burnt-out farmhouses alone inviting though it may seem to some. Because, booby-trapped in the most cunning of ways most of them certainly were. And that would have meant someone going with him. Because that was the drill. No one went anywhere in Normandy alone. Mind you, I don't think somehow they had looting in mind, when they made that rule. Anyway, it stilled this thumping from within me for the moment at least. Because I most certainly wouldn't have let young Sonny go. I didn't intend to let it be seen that I was as scared as all that even if I was. So once more it looked as though it would have to be me again.

The three of us sat and waited trying not to breathe in too much, so as not to inhale the stench of those trapped animal gases that had been suddenly expelled into the atmosphere. Smithy jumped off the carrier on to the road, holding his nose. "You'll not get me drinking any more Bovril or Oxo cubes from now on, you can bet your life on that" It was a typical Smithy remark, but for once nobody was laughing." What the hell's the matter with everybody?" he smirked, still holding his long thin nose. "We're all stuck here like the Three Bloody Stooges. Only, if I remember rightly, at least two of them had some hair. We've got buggerall. We're scalped." As indeed we all were then in those last days in Aldershot . . .

He was right of course. All our heads had been shorn. The order had been given just before we began training for D Day, and in a way it made us all look alike, although in Smithy's case you could still denote a fair sheen below his scalp which told you that on his bonce there was still a considerable amount of hair there which was only just in keeping and no more with the Kings rules and regulations with regards to army hair cuts.

Sonny and myself were the opposite, both dark-haired also visible at the roots. Those close cropped cuts we were forced to have for D Day reminded me that there was something else we had all forgotten to do before leaving Aldershot, and that was to enquire how a certain sergeant major's health had ever since we left for Normandy. For that particular S.M. had gone out of his way to make life hell for a lot of us whilst we were all busy *Bostiking* up our vehicles for the Channel crossing…

… And of course because he knew only too well that he wouldn't be going over with us he felt he had nothing to fear in the way of reprisals. Being a Resident Training Instructor (amongst other things) he had nothing to lose and acted accordingly. Not only on the barrack square but outside too, in the Naafi, in the street, and the dining hall. Everywhere in fact.

They reckoned that even his own R.S.M. didn't want to know him. Some other sergeants gave him a wide berth too. He was forever going on at length about he himself being a real soldier, meaning of course that he'd been a Regular Soldier, and had done fifteen years. Smithy said to him and he heard him, "It should have been fucking life, you bastard" and got a week confined for his comments. But Smithy still maintained it was well worth it.

This said sergeant major whose name escapes me was forever bragging that he had joined the army when Britain was needing men, and not just feeding them! He always seemed to think that was a funny quote and waited for someone to laugh having said it. But nobody ever did. And that infuriated him even more. So much so that an incident occurred one summer night in the run up to D Day.

Our particular platoon had been housed up at the top of the six storeys of the large barrack building there. Each one of the steps up were made of wrought iron which made one helluva noise as one could well imagine. Your feet clattered when you went up and your feet clattered when you came down. They clattered even more when someone else came down whether by accident or "design".

Now it appears that a certain group of soldiers who shall also be nameless, had been celebrating with abandon one night when a certain sergeant major went out of his way to stick his oar in. Now it is said that those same soldiers knowing that Normandy beckoned, forcibly ejected that very same S.M. out of a billet which was perilously near the top of those wrought iron stairs and more or less helped him on his way down. Arguments and curses had seemingly filled the night air. And singing voices too could be detected. The last sound that was heard was one of bump, bump, bump as he hit each landing of those wrought iron stairs on the way down. Army boots and wrought iron could be an awesome combination . . .

It could well have been the sound of a body, one helpful soldier just below that top flat admitted the next day to the two Redcaps who were investigating the incident. And yes, after giving the matter a bit of thought now that those good M.P.s mentioned it, there had been a lot of shouting too, the soldier was at length to tell them. However he was sorry that although he had heard a lot he hadn't actually seen anything. And he agreed with those investigating M.P.s that it was rather remiss of him not to have seen anyone that night since it had been a bright summer evening.

Then that same soldier remembered that he had probably been cleaning his webbing and polishing his equipment at that particular time. Yes that was probably what he was doing at the time. And yes though he hated to admit it, it was something he liked doing of an evening . . . And most certainly much better than sitting in the Naafi drinking beer all night . . . But after hearing the sound of a body being bumped down the stairs? Hadn't he heard anything else? Yes, now that they had brought it up, there had been a certain amount of noise after the incident. "Noise?" they asked. "What kind of noise?" "Was it possible for him to remember?"

"Come to think it, y-es. It just sounded like soldiers singing!" He wasn't sure of the tune. But it was definitely singing! No. He didn't think it was "For He's A Jolly Good Fellow." He was adamant about that. However if he could hazard a guess?" Well it was a song not unlike "Old Soldiers –" "Old Soldiers Never Die?" blurted out one of the two brighter of the M.Ps. Could it possibly have been that? He didn't know about the "never die" bit of the song. However, he did hear words like "Fade Away" and "Old Soldier" but then he couldn't be sure.

Could he? A sergeant major. You say? Well I never . . . Whatever next . . . The squaddie was so terribly sorry he couldn't have been more helpful. But then again like he's said he'd been spit and polishing all night. Hadn't he? . . .

. . . No. Hitler had been by no means the only enemy of our time! . . . But all that stuff was behind us now, sergeant majors and soldiers with close-cropped hair couldn't have been further from anyone's mind at that particular moment. It may well have been that almost unbearable smell of rotting cattle and the sweet sickly smell of hastily interred humans like ourselves but Smithy just wasn't prepared to wait any longer, not for me, not for Pricey, not for anyone. He had the scent of loot once more in his nostrils. And this put me in a dilemma. Not to go with him, and I knew his mind was made up, would be to show my reluctance in front of a very young Sonny. Thus leaving him to draw his own conclusions. And yet at the same time to accompany Smithy could be interpreted as condoning the disobeying of orders. There was just no way I was going to win.

I tried once more to make Smithy listen to reason "Come on," I coaxed. "You know fine that Price could be back at any minute, and what then?" He shook his head firmly. "I couldn't give a monkeys. I'm off." I looked over at Sonny who was busying himself cleaning the gun. "Let him go. It's his problem. But if you want to go with him, go. I'll try and hold the fort until you get back. But you'd better make it quick!"

He seemed to appreciate the predicament I was in. I nodded my head. "Thanks." I then jumped off the carrier and joined Smithy "Let's get on with it then," I said angrily, "and get it over with. But this better be the last time. Because I don't intend to get my head blown off for you or anyone else. Got that!" And it did appear for a moment that he had got the message. So off we went.

It was comparatively easy to move about without too many others noticing us because nothing was happening. Our whole operation had somehow been brought to a halt. Everything had that static look. Apart from the occasional eighty-eight being fired back at us from hastily retreating Germans there was nothing of any note occurring. Some crews glad of the lull were attending to much needed vehicle repairs. Some catching up on some sleep were slumped behind their driving wheels. Some were just sat there waiting for the Call. So we moved in and out and around armoured cars, tanks and other vehicles with ease. Then crossing over a field dodging dead cattle as best we could, we headed for a farmhouse in the distance that Smithy had already earmarked for "investigation".

The nearer the farmhouse we got the more excited Smithy became as we crouch-walked training fashion, behind the low wall at the bottom of the backyard. Raising our heads over so slightly we saw that the yard was littered with pots and pans.

Alongside lay a couple of barrels on their side. Empty I thought, but you never could tell. Little trickles of liquid were still dribbling out of one of them. They certainly weren't worth checking out and I indicated this to Smithy silently. Then he spotted a little hut with the roof hanging off "Look. A hen-house". Before I could say a word he was leaning over and inside. He then stuck his hand in and held up a couple of eggs triumphantly. "I told you, didn't I?" I said nothing.

A weather-cock whirled away merrily on top of what was a barn of some sort. Irrelevant it may have been but at least it added something positive to what was virtually an atmosphere of unreality if nothing else. And bloody Smithy had dragged me into this dangerous vacuum. However, there could be no turning back now. Still he'd better be quick. I checked my watch. If Pricey was back and found that we'd beat it leaving just Sonny in charge we could be in big trouble. And I'd be in it up to my neck even more for accompanying him. But I most certainly wasn't going to tell him that Smithy would have gone on his own anyway, no matter what.

Anyway with our rifles at the ready we moved with stealth around the fading white painted wall of the farmhouse "Let's call it a day and get back," I hissed into Smithy's ear. "From where I'm standing there's nothing worthwhile here. Anything worth taking has already been nicked." Smithy was having none of it. "Let's have a quick shufti inside and if we don't find anything we're out straight away and back to the carrier. OK?"

I settled for that and we moved on further still hugging the wall with Smithy leading the way. We encountered a door. Dark green at one time it may well have been, but the ancient paint-work was now in an advanced state of peeling as befitted the occasion I recall thinking at the time. Smithy pushed the old rusty latch upwards. It creaked open. Then picking up a stone that was lying at his feet he pushed the door open quickly and hurled the stone inside. He clapped two hands to his ears instantly and held them there for a few seconds. He then turned round and gave me the thumbs up sign. "We're OK." My heart was pumping fit to burst, but again I said nothing. As far as I was concerned it was his show with myself a mere observer. And once again I wished I wasn't, for he'd forgotten already what I'd told him about the futility of trying to jump clear after the event.

We stepped inside hands firmly on rifles but hearts not so firmly in place. Mine anyway most certainly not. Smithy looked calm. I hated saying it, but I admired his guts. To be fair he was taking great care, but I still stuck to that reasonable distance between him and me. We entered a long narrow room and there in the centre, was a large, oblong, mahogany type table. The table dominated the whole place.

An open fireplace with a basket of logs alongside ran the table a close second in order of merit. This was undoubtedly the kitchen.

There was no tablecloth on the table. All that lay on top was a few dirty dishes and a few cups and saucers. One cup lay up-turned as though it had been hastily discarded. A large copper coloured coffee-pot also vied for status on that handsome table. I did a bit of detective work and felt the pot to see if it was still hot. It was stone cold. Exit Sherlock Holmes.

Smithy was also tentatively sniffing at teacups. He then began to lift the lid off a little white sugar bowl. "Surely you're not thinking of nicking sugar, Smithy?" He glared back at me reprovingly. "No, I'm not thinking of nicking bloody sugar," he sneered. "I'm merely testing for valuables. Because if there was any jewels or valuables that's where they'd be. In places you'd least expect to find them, see! Saw it in an Edgar Wallace film." So spoke the voice of authority. He was now opening bottles that stood on a kind of display cabinet beside the table. Most were empty but one decanter he sniffed at seemed to command his attention. He beckoned me over. "Smell that. That's brandy, isn't it?" He held the bottle up to the light. There were things floating about inside the bottle "Here Mac. What do you think? Looks like hazelnuts to me. I think I'll have a swig and see what it's like." Again I stood firm. "Swig away," I said. "You can even have my share. I'm staying put."

What would be his next move I wondered. My watch said we'd been away for almost an hour. I couldn't believe we'd been away that long. What if Pricey was back and we were not? Even worse I thought. What if he was back. And we were holding up the main convoy advance? Could be tantamount to desertion. I dared not dwell on the implications of it all. I decided there and then that enough was enough and indicated as much to Smithy just as he was preparing to open another potentially booby-trapped cupboard and to throw himself backwards..

"You can blow yourself up if you want, Smithy, but I'm off back now. The whole convoy could be about to move off without us." "Bollocks," he retorted, picking himself back up off the floor. "OK then," I said. " Please yourself but I'm off now. " He knew then I was serious." "OK" he replied. "Let's have one last quick look upstairs." But I shook my head firmly and turned to go. Then the incorrigible Smithy decided to have one last go and with bated breath he tried to prise open yet another cupboard door. But alas that cupboard too was bare . "That's it," I shouted. "No more of this bloody upstairs downstairs stuff, I'm off now", I cried as he put one foot on the bottom stair about to ascend. I then headed for another door, which I took to be the back door, which was also badly in need of a coat of paint. Funny the stupid things you notice when it's the last thing you should be noticing. But I'd made my point. Smithy was behind me. And for once had taken my lead. I pushed the door open and it was then I froze! As did Smithy!

Instinctively our hands went to our rifles and for a second I couldn't breathe. There was no mistaking that greyish green uniform. Nor was there any movement from the occupants of those uniforms. They were motionless and they were dead. They had to be. But we would have to ensure that such was the case. So it was hands firmly on rifles again but this time with a bit more conviction. Could be a ruse of sorts again? If it wasn't then we could be the dead ones. My heart was thumping thirteen to the dozen. And although I knew him to be a perfectly stable type, I was sure Smithy's heart was beating every bit as hard as mine.

Then I surprised even myself by taking the initiative. Despite the constant throbbing within me and watched by an ashen-faced Smithy I prodded that green uniformed rear as hard as I could with my rifle. Then stood back. But there was no reaction. It was as though my rifle had run up against something solid. Was this rigor mortis? I wondered. I did the same to that other very erect back and got the same response. I coaxed some very welcome saliva back to my lips. There was no doubt about it. Those two German soldiers we'd encountered were very dead; the best possible kind. Would that we could find more in that non combat state.

Their bodies rested where they'd stood. Their fronts supported by a brick wall about five feet high which had been built opposite the back door. The wall looked to have been just recently built. Whether it had been built to keep out draughts from whistling through the back door or purpose built to be a sort of parapet from where one could pick off potential enemies we shall never know.

Whatever the reason it hadn't saved those two German soldiers. But where were their rifles? They were not to be seen. A quick search of their persons proved fruitless. And what was even more curious. Could they possibly be deserters? Oh yes, the Germans had them too. And they may well have just decided that enough was enough when our troops landed yesterday and indeed were still in the process of landing and had thrown their weapons away hoping to be captured instead of being killed. But it hadn't quite worked out for them, had it? Someone or something had got to them first and to all intents and purposes they had been unprepared for it.

We then went round the outside of the wall to see what we could see and I for one wished I hadn't. You can never get used to seeing dead bodies no matter how often you see them. A Wehrmacht kepi with a highly polished badge on it was still perched on a white face that had been literally halved in two and wedged in the corner of that half a mouth was what looked to me like a cigarette butt. The other soldier's head was bowed. They must have been tall men. For both their heads were above the parapet and looking outwards. There was congealed blood beside the soldier whose head was bowed. It was as though the wall and his shoulders were all that was supporting that head from becoming detached from the rest of the body.

We looked no more and took a decision to leave them where we'd found them in their perpendicular open-air grave. I couldn't help but feel sorry for them. They were two young Wehrmacht soldiers cut down by person or persons unknown. And judging by the evidence of their bodies it was obvious they had fallen foul of a grenade or a mortar attack. But the absence of any weapons was undoubtedly a mystery. Given up? Thrown their guns away? Human?

We made our way back the same way we had come. The Germans were still firing back in anger rather than with accuracy as we wended our way back in and out of vehicles to Sonny and our carrier position. Young Sonny welcomed us back. His face said it all. Pricey was still in conference, thank God. So no harm done there I thought. Smithy climbed in and took up position behind the wheel.

Just what were those two Germans doing in that farmhouse? I wondered. Smithy too probably. Because he did look a bit pensive from where I was sitting. Then it struck me. If he was honest with himself he could come to one and only one conclusion. Try as I might I myself could not come up with any kind of explanation for the absence of their rifles. But there was no doubt what those two German soldiers were after.

They too had been chasing something. And that something was nothing more and nothing less than loot! The very same commodity Smithy had been chasing. For as we were going in one door of that farmhouse those same two Germans had been going out another door some thirty-six hours or so earlier. Or at least that was the plan until fate in whatever disguise be it mortar or be it shell, had taken a hand in affairs. There was a lesson I thought be learned in there somewhere . . .

Pricey was with us again. Almost as suddenly he was called away to what he told us was to be a top-level briefing. He beckoned Smithy to get on the carrier and behind the wheel. Then an out-of-breath Pricey gave it to us straight. "Listen; we've captured Caen, well almost. There's still some fighting going on. But we've got infantry in there and they're holding out till we get there to reinforce, along with our artillery." We listened intently, as he went on. "You're not going to believe this and that's why I was so long away. Montgomery was there." "Don't know him," said Smithy. "General Montgomery, you clot." hissed Price, clenching a fist in Smithy's direction. "Came in at the last minute. Told us to keep our chins up and that it could all be over in about three months." Smithy looked over at him again. "You should have asked him to give you it in bloody writing."

The call came about half an hour later and we moved forward; carriers, tanks, and armoured cars together with Bedford trucks full of infantrymen. And the target? None other than Caen. The convoy moved on steadily averaging an agonising five miles an hour without any resistance. The only halts we had were waiting for burnt-out tanks, and overturned cars armoured and otherwise to be cleared. It was obvious too that some of those more private cars had been commandeered. And by the brand names they bore not by us.

As we neared the medieval town of Caen we were almost overwhelmed by German troops running towards us on either side of the road hands on heads to indicate surrender if such a movement was needed. Walking wasn't quick enough for some of them as they jostled to get past. Shock, bewilderment and open-mouthed. Those were the expressions on those extremely young German faces as they strove to get as far away as possible from it all. Little wonder. Caen had taken a real pounding from our artillery. The results of which, we were to see later.

*"Wir Kommen Wieder."* The Germans Trade Mark. Or *"We will be Back."* That was the greeting that was printed in letters about three feet high on a wall in the old town's centre. We were ordered off trucks and took up positions lying beside our vehicles. Because it was a favourite trick of the Germans to vacate a town deliberately and retreat to a mile or so outside. But before retreating, precise readings would be taken and salient points noted along with landmarks. Then they would endeavour to plaster the new unsuspecting inhabitants from their new vantage point from outside. And it almost worked again. But we were getting better and better. Learning fast. And if the number of prisoners we encountered on our way to Caen were anything to go by it was just possible the Germans were running out of manpower.

Refugees were to be the next problem for the Allies. The townspeople of Caen, already sick at the sight of their once beautiful old town being almost razed to the ground, began to crowd round our vehicles pleading for somewhere to go in case the Germans started attacking again. Most of them had no homes to go to. We did what we could, and advised them to stay under cover as best they could.

But there wasn't a lot that they could do. So between a spell of shelling some of us, officers and men alike decided to help them out a little.

And we came up with what we thought was a good idea. One of the least damaged buildings turned out to be the town hall. So the mayor was approached and he finally relented. We all did our bit one way or another, and cleaned up the place for them. And they were eternally grateful. Some of those mademoiselles were even more eternally grateful than others so Smithy, myself and a few others strove with all our hearts and other equally important assets to assuage their thanks as best we could.

Then it was north to Amiens. The chase was well and truly on. Monty could yet be proved right. It looked as if it was all going to be straightforward all the way. We were rolling on relentlessly. There appeared to be nothing to stop us. It looked as though the only thing that could halt us would be the usual pile of wreckage we were encountering on the road. There were also hordes of running Germans who couldn't wait to be taken prisoner but were more or less throwing themselves at us begging to be taken away from it all.

But we had no time for such niceties especially to the Germans. We leapt on and off carrier whenever the chance arose to relieve a passing prisoner of a wrist-watch or two, which they seemed to have in abundance, not to mention the occasional camera. And I was in there too as eager and as greedy as the rest. As indeed was Pricey, who should have known better, as Section Leader. And who should have been setting an example to the rest of us. Because he knew, as we all did, that it was against regulations to relieve prisoners of their property.

But then that 's the way it was then at that precise moment in time. It was the law of the jungle. We were taking everything we could, and thrusting aside anything that stood in our way. Everything suddenly was going our way. We were the victors and they the vanquished. It was simple as that. We were racing on to Amiens without even as much as a sight of the enemy. Montgomery's prophecy was going to be proved correct. The Germans were in total retreat. We could all be home by Christmas. Maybe even before that. Each and every one of us began to get caught up in the fever and the excitement of it all. We were beginning to taste victory. An infection was setting in. And we were all smitten.

Amiens had also been vacated by the Germans, only this time they hadn't posted their usual warning. *"We Will Be Back."* Once again it was festival time. We were feted by the townsfolk of Amiens with flowers being thrown up to us as we raced in triumphantly on carriers tanks and armoured cars. They lined the streets cheering as though the war had suddenly been declared to be over.

Triumphalism was rampant. There was no doubt about that, but over confidence reared it's ugly head again. The cheering had hardly died down before we were scurrying for cover once more. The retreating Germans were at their old tricks again and began plastering us from a hill overlooking the town. Heavy eighty-eights and mortars bombarded us and celebrations had to be suspended till they retreated further back which they eventually did. A calm spell then ensued allowing us a very much-needed respite.

We, as a Specialised Vickers Machine Gun Section, ex Argylls, and now part of the Royal Northumberland Fusiliers were all under the umbrella of the Eleventh Armoured Division and had been since it's formation some months before D Day. And of this we were justly proud. But that pride was about to take a knock. Because we were about to play second fiddle to none other than the Guards Armoured Division. Tradition. Red tape. Bullshit. Or just a sniff of royalty. Call it what you will. Anyway it was about to rear it's ugly even regal, head.

Whilst we were succumbing to the welcome of the citizens of Amiens, it transpired that top level talks were taking place as to the next move in this war game. It was generally acknowledged that the Germans were now in total retreat, and that "The End" was in sight. But, the blue-blooded, top-drawer division were about to make a decision. And that decision was that if there had to be an ending; it would be a Royal Ending. Therefore, rather than let the Eleventh Armoured race from Amiens to liberate Brussels it was decreed that instead it would be the Guards Armoured who would do the needful. The Eleventh Armoured would take Antwerp instead. Nothing like a happy, but Royal Ending . . . What ho chaps . . . !!

Now we were led to believe that it was the Eleventh that would race to liberate Brussels and not the Guards. But then they say that you shouldn't believe everything you hear. But that's the story we heard first and our lot chose rightly or wrongly, to believe our version. But anyway, it wasn't the time for sulking. Both divisions would leave Amiens at a synchronised time to race on Brussels and Antwerp in a bid to force the German army back still further into Holland and then into the Fatherland if necessary. We left Amiens to the cheers of the locals.

They were obviously under the same opinion as we were that the war was drawing to an end. I sincerely hoped that they were right. Things were looking good. The Ardennes fiasco had been righted. The Yanks had been pointed in the right direction. They had also been coaxed to stop taking photographs of each other sitting on top of tanks and hoisting the Stars and Stripes especially when they had just dug themselves into new positions and were still in sight of the Germans.

It was even rumoured that some American generals had agreed albeit reluctantly to remove one row of their medals from their much be-ribboned chests. This in itself must have lightened the load on their vehicles considerably thus speeding up the advance of the entire division! We entered Antwerp on a bright sunny Sunday morning to the ringing of church bells. Birds were singing as though ordered specially to do just that on time. The Antwerpens lined the streets waving and cheering and trying to clamber aboard our vehicles. They threw flowers, and blew kisses. They shouted and whistled. In between the bells ringing and the shouts and cheers of the crowd, we managed to get hugs and kisses from those lovely people as our vehicles ground to a halt.

They jumped aboard and more or less took over from us, smothering us with more and more kisses. Smithy was in his element. None of us were complaining either. Unfortunately however we were not allowed off our vehicles. Checks had to be made despite an assurance from no less a personage than the mayor of Antwerp himself that the last German officer had left the city at 6a.m. that morning. Had he signed the visitor's book I wondered? Antwerp had also taken it's fair share of bombs and mortars. But despite the damage done to her, Antwerp had it's own particular brand of beauty and charm.

Like the Free State of Ireland, Antwerp had signposts printed in two languages; French and Flemish. And this endeared the city to me due to my Irish parentage. Antwerpen, was the Flemish name for Antwerp; and Anviers, was the French title granted to that fine city with her fine cathedral-like churches. In fact the one in the city centre with one of the tallest steeples I had ever seen may well have been a cathedral. Not being an architect or an expert in church design I don't suppose I shall ever know. But one thing I did know. In fact, one thing we were told in no uncertain terms, that they most certainly did have, was A Zoo . . .

Now, zoos had never been my cup of tea even as a child. It's quite possible however that it could well have been had my parents ever had enough money in those days to send all seven of us to such a place of entertainment. "You must come to see our beautiful zoo" the people kept telling us. "You have seen nothing till you have seen our zoo!"

Lions and tigers weren't exactly high on my list of priorities as to what I would like to see in the foreseeable future. And it was obvious that Smithy, Sonny and Price couldn't have cared less either, but we kept humouring our hosts. "Yes, we shall come to see your beautiful zoo as soon as we can." "Our zoo is one of the biggest in all Europe." "Yes, I'm sure it is." We had to keep the natives happy somehow, and anyway we were desperate to get out of those vehicles and stretch our legs a little. But then again to our surprise it was all change, once more.

Pricey had again been called over with our platoon commander to a meeting in the town centre. We waited his return somewhat impatiently still promising fervently to the Antwerpens that we would visit their zoo. Pricey jumped aboard five minutes later and shouted to Smithy. "Turn the carrier!" Smithy did as he was told, then awaited further instructions. "Now, follow that three ton Bedford in front. And don't lose him." Giving a driver like Smithy instructions like that was tantamount to saying. "Drive as fast as you bloody well can. But if you've got to injure some of us, I'll settle for just a broken arm, if you don't mind." So we held on like we were used to doing as Smithy followed, or should I say as our carrier's nose began scraping the back of that Bedford.

"Where are we headed for anyway?" shouted Smithy inclining his head backwards but still keeping on top of that Bedford, in the full sense of the term. "The bloody zoo. I haven't got the slightest idea why. We were just told to get down there." We were about five miles out of town, when a sign said it all. Zoological Gardens. So we followed that Bedford and into the Zoological Gardens of Antwerp. Just before we dismounted, I quickly checked the back of that Bedford. And yes. There was a slight, but still discernible scratch on it. That's my Smithy, I thought, to myself.

Now we all knew why all the natives or should I say most of those Antwerpens, wanted us to see their famous zoo. Because, believe you me, that zoo had everything, lions, tigers, and bears. AND PEOPLE. Yes, people. As a matter of fact people predominated behind those bars in those gigantic cages. At first glance it was very difficult to comprehend what was happening. What was all this in aid of? There were scores of people inside those cages, and there were scores of people outside those cages. And those outside the cages were shouting, and throwing stones, and even garbage, at those inside who were gesticulating just as furiously at those outside.

Then it was all explained to us by the furious multitude outside the cages. All those inside were said to be known collaborators. They had been accused of consorting, or co-habiting, if you will with the Germans. And this was their punishment. To be locked in cages for the rest of their lives. "Very cosy. Very cosy indeed," laughed Smithy when the penny finally dropped. "I can think of a few bloody N.C.O.s who could fit nicely into some of those cages." Pricey gave him a curious sort of look so Smithy didn't elaborate. It was certainly a strange situation.

Just imagine being suddenly caged in a zoo by people and neighbours you had known all your life. But that's exactly how it was that Sunday morning in Antwerp.

Not only that but we noticed that some of the women had been shorn of their hair and had been cropped even shorter than the style we were sporting at that particular time. This particular punishment was reserved seemingly for the women who had had some sort of relationship with German soldiers. May even have had the gall to fall in love with some of them. Obviously that old proverb about her hair being a woman's crowning glory did not apply in this particular instance. To my mind however it certainly was the cruellest of cruel ways to wreak vengeance however justifiable some may think it was.

And justifiable was obviously the key word here. And that was why our commanding officer had ordered us down to the zoo. Who was to say who was right and who was wrong in these cases? It could all be a ploy to get even with someone for some reason or other or just plain jealousy. And our C.O. was having none of it. Fair Play chaps and all that. But in this instance even I had to admit he was doing the right thing. So after a conference with a priest and a couple of town officials he demanded the keys and threw the cages open despite vehement protests. In fact one chubby little person in the crowd started waving a huge pair of shears angrily at our actions. He wasn't pleased. That's for sure. "You know why he's angry, don't you?" said Smithy. "No why?" asked young Sonny, anxiously." Because he'll be out of a bloody job now that's why. He'll be the town barber. It's as plain as the nose on your face." Few of us would have argued with that.

My lasting impression of that zoo, of those cages and all those angry faces was of a young, beautiful, fair-haired girl who couldn't have been any more than sixteen. She sat in a corner of one of the cages crying her eyes out, ruefully fingering the inch-long stubs of what once was her pride and joy. What was *her* particular war crime I wondered? . . .

But there was no time to dwell for too long on such happenings. It was war once more. And the move was now on to end it once and for all. Brussels, as well as Antwerp had both been liberated. The German war machine was in full retreat. It will all be over long before Christmas. Again this was the message that was emanating from reliable sources. Another story that was beginning to take credence was that Hitler had already surrendered. Another whisper was that he had been assassinated. We would have settled for either. But no one was really caring now. So confident were we that our platoon received a visit from an army dentist.

No, not to pull any teeth but to take details of what was required regarding fillings and mouth inspections etc. It was all a build-up he informed us to ensure that we went back to Civvy Street prepared for anything.

"I'll settle for that," said Smithy thumping one fist into the other. "I'm not really worried whether they pull the bloody lot out or not as long as I can get back to Brummie." We slept easily that night knowing that in the morning baring accidents and a sudden turn around military wise we would be heading for Holland. And then unless something unforeseen happened there would be nothing to prevent us pouring across the river bloody Rhine. Our confidence cup was overflowing again. Celtic Park here I come!

*Little old me with no wrinkles*

*Reflections*

*The Platoon...The Vickers...And those bloody Tripods.*

*Flensburg, with suitable foreground.*

*Patrolling Flensburg, in pairs, as it had to be in the early days.*

*Celebrating with my wife shortly after the war...*

*Beauty and the Beach...*

# Parents Told "Gun Shield" He'd Won M.M.

*BY AN EASTERN STANDARD STAFF REPORTER.*

THE parents of Fus. Edward McCann, 256 Warriston st., Carntyne, have had the unique pleasure of being the first to tell their son of his award of the Military Medal.

One morning, recently, a letter was delivered at the McCann's house, addressed to Mrs. McCann. She opened it and read: "Dear Mrs. McCann, I am pleased to inform you that your son has been awarded the M.M. for gallantry.

"As I do not know his exact whereabouts I should be glad if you would pass on this information to him.

"Your son won this award on October 13, 1944. With total disregard for his own safety he used himself as a shield for a machine-gun crew and also held the gun firm on the ground to enable it to fire accurately. But for his action this gun would not have been able to be fired at a critical time.

"At present your son is recuperating from the after-effects of battle strain and I hope that he will have recovered entirely very soon. He is badly missed by

*Extract from newspaper article, October 1945.*

*Cutting that 50th Anniversary Cake.*

## Chapter Six

*Those Nasty Nazis But Not So Nasty Frauleins*

. . . My head and my heart were still very much in Antwerp and it would not be easily dispelled even as our train pulled out of Hamburg's Hauptbahnhof and slowly headed north, and from what I'd heard and read it was the only way to do it. We were about to venture into the home of Germany's National Socialism, Schleswig Holstein. Some may even say it was the stronghold of the Nazi Party because Schleswig Holstein was fiercely fertile country. It was lush and plentiful; full of all the good things in life that Adolf wanted for that Nazi Party of his. And his wish had certainly been granted for it was undoubtedly one of the crowns in many of the jewels he craved. But unfortunately for him history was now telling him that it was not to be.

The corridor windows were crammed to capacity again as we began to cast an eye over one of the better rural segments of the master race. As the weather improved so did the sights from our vantage point through those corridor windows. It most certainly was a big, big country. And it had to be stressed that we were only seeing a very small part of it. We were barely an hour out of Hamburg, when the sheer greenery of those small but economically packaged pasture lands began to win us over. Notwithstanding, we were all desperate to see just what made those Germans tick.

Our first stop was Neumunster, a somewhat sombre stop for us with the locals' faces matching their predicament. So they had lost the war but the damage done to them didn't seem half as bad as many others that we'd seen. They watched in awe as we pulled out. I got the impression that they were weighing up the chances of stoning our train and getting away with it. However they didn't . . .

The landscape took on an even more illustrious look as our train headed towards Rendsburg famous for it's stupendously high bridge woven into the figure eight away up in that German sky. It was a suspension bridge which gave you an aerial picture of Rendsburg from what I reckoned to be about two or three hundred feet up. The train weaved her way understandably slowly right the way round that intricate digit eight. And it drew thankful gasps from all of us as we looked out and down through those train windows. All we could see were people way down below us crawling in and out and around little square patches of green and yellow. Awesome!

Further along past Rendsburg we were to watch a dexterity in diving that to my eyes at least must have been world class. Youngsters were diving from a great height off a bridge into the Kiel Canal. You could love those German youths or hate them but to my eyes what we were witnessing was grace, beauty and skill, all rolled into one for all to see. Showing off maybe. But impressive certainly. Those lithe young bodies with hair almost yellow in hue were obviously out to show us that the famous or infamous Hitler Youth Movement was still very much alive and kicking and swimming.

We were still spectating as our train quickened up somewhat and headed for Flensburg that most northern of German towns lying cheek by jowl with neutral Denmark. It was all uphill at first. But then our journey gradually got better in the fullest sense of the word. Even when we were still about ten kilometres away from Flensburg everything suddenly became serene and beautiful with hardly a thing out of place. In fact it was hard to believe that utter and complete devastation was only about fifty or sixty kilometres away to the south. It was like coming straight out of hell and into heaven and the weather was kind to us as we rolled. Things were beginning to look up.

Flensburg was a beautiful albeit a typical little German town situated on the Ostzee or the East Sea and was a small tributary of the North Sea and a Frontier town to boot. The Danish border was about a mile further north. Flensburg boasted an opera house, a rum distillery and a brewery. And that had to be a very good start. It was also a town steeped in history, intrigue and controversy. For every half century or so they would have what was called a plebiscite; that being a kind of vote to see if Flensburg wished to become part of Denmark or remain still part of Germany. And from what I gathered they always voted to remain German. And the Danes resented this deeply according to the locals. Which begs the question. Why didn't the Danes vote for it then?

It wasn't surprising therefore that they hated each other's guts. Yet if you happened to walk along Flensburg's Hohe Strasse or any other street for that matter you would be surprised when you looked up to see who those shops belonged to. The names above those shop doors would be a Thomsen, a Jansen, a Christiansen or a Johansen. In other words, they were all Danish Names. Obviously there was something wrong somewhere.

We were soon to find out all about the vagaries of those Germans and their next door neighbours, the Danes. And this was reflected in their shopping habits. These were erratic to say the least. The Danes would make the short distance over to Flensburg by ferry or road or by train to buy such things as butter, sugar and eggs. Whereas the Flensburger on the other hand, would go over to Denmark and buy mainly clothes and zigaretten in Denmark where it would appear they were much cheaper. Crazy ecomomics no matter which way you looked at it.

No I know what you're thinking. A veritable fountainhead of useless knowledge? Maybe so but it was information from an old book about Germany; Schleswig Holstein in particular, some time ago. And I digested what I could in between referring to my English\German\French phrase book which I'd just happened to have taken from a German prisoner of war,.

Needless to say, this information was unknown to me, when I first arrived in Flensburg. What I did get to know and it pleased me no end was that my very own Eleventh Armoured Division was already there in Flensburg. At least some of them were. I knew a few of them by sight. But unfortunately there were none of my old company there, let alone any of my old platoon. But I was told later that quite a lot of troops had been recalled back to the U.K. So they couldn't be specific as to just who they were.

But who was I to try and pick their brains. I would meet the fearsome threesome all in good time. Suffice to be satisfied they had all got through it. And could only hope that the list I had managed to read on the train was up to date. And why shouldn't it be up to date? The war had ended just shortly after. Hadn't it? Surely they'd all managed to keep their heads down until that final whistle had blown. Already established there when I arrived in Flensburg, were some soldiers from the Tank Regiment, some of whom I knew by sight.

Also there were some artillery people, again from the Eleventh Armoured, whom I could only vaguely remember, but who assured me that my mates would turn up all right like the proverbial bad penny. They did stress however that everything had been so chaotic after that final whistle had been blown but they tried to assure me that losses had not been as bad as had been predicted. Although they also said that they had to pinch each other to reassure themselves that they had managed to come through it all unscathed. I could only hope to God they were right, and weren't just stringing me along. I would certainly keep my eyes open for them. And that first pint with those infamous three would be like savouring nectar with the gods. Mind you that didn't alter the fact that I would still have to see them with my own eyes before I could be sure that they had made it safely through to the bitter end. If they had, the next thing would be to find out where they had all been dispersed to. Whether it was back to the U.K, or installed in another part of Germany or whatever. They may even be already demobbed. Those indeed were the questions that had to be answered.

But oh what I would have given to have met even one of them right bang there in Flensburg and to be able to have that drink. It would have been great to be able to talk and to discuss just what actually happened that horrific night in Overloon.

But deep down I knew the odds of them all being in Flensburg at the same time would have been astronomical. Still they couldn't stop a bloke dreaming could they?

Just to be able to listen in once more to that non-stop Brummie patter of Smithy's would have been something. And to savour once more that sharp wit of his which seemed to match that sharp pointed nose of his. For whether they were back home or still in Germany no one deserved to be back alive more than those three glorious musketeers.

I was now a humble private with the R.A.S.C. E.F.I. Or to give that mouthful it's proper title; The Royal Army Service Corps (Expeditionary Forces). In other words the Naafi no less And often I've tried to conjure up what kind of capital Smithy would have made of it all, if I ever had the good fortune to come across him again. "I always knew you were a bit of a Naafi tart you little Scotch git!" would probably have been his reaction. We had been expeditiously formed to serve as the Army of Occupation in Germany. In other words we were to satisfy their every need food wise and drink wise. We had already had taken over the local brewery. And we had also annexed Flensburg's Brauerei, and a good drop of stuff it was too. The troops loved it, scoffing pint after pint of the stuff night after night. And no one grudged them it one little bit. I only hoped that some of our lot made it soon, then we could all celebrate.

We were empowered also to take on local labour to help us when and wherever needed. And we did just that. The army commandeered a night club in Flensburg, and used it as a canteen. A splendid place it was too where the boys could sit and chat over tea and wads or over a pint of beer. We had an Irish sergeant in charge and I was delegated as acting Lance Corporal to be his next in command. We employed local bakers to bake nice cakes and rolls etc, and we hired waitresses from the very few local frauleins who applied for work.

Being virtually untouched by bombing of any sort and being the gateway to Denmark, Flensburg had become the target for all sorts of Displaced Persons. Not least of all for those top nazis like Admiral Raeder and other top naval people looking for some sort of hiding place. Although Flensburg was a bi-zonal town it was treated no better than any other German town; and would be answerable to the Local Military Government.

A Black Market was now beginning to emerge. And German cameras were at a premium, the German Leica being the Rolls Royce of them all, so sought after by so many and prized enough to even kill for. But the most prized treasure of them all just had to be those delectable frauleins. They were indeed the most real, the most coveted, and out-shone anything else. You could forget the pre-war Hollywood stars like Carole Lombard, or even our very own Margaret Lockwood, for those frauleins were the best many of us had ever seen.

We were briefed to let the Flensburgers get on with their lives as far as was humanly possible and this was seen as an honest attempt by our Regional Military Government to get everything back to normal. Shops and businesses were allowed to carry on business as before so long as they kept within the guidelines laid down by us. But we all had a right to stop and search the many civilians and wounded soldiers if we felt that it was necessary, and in many cases it was essential.

There were so many wounded soldiers still in uniform roaming the streets at night that keeping check was almost impossible. Some of those pathetic cases had only one arm, and some only one leg. There was even some I spotted with no legs at all, hobbling around on make-shift crutches. If there was ever proof needed that losing wars didn't pay this was the place to come to. Because in Flensburg just after the war was the place to be if you wanted ever to meet someone who was worse off than yourself.

But worst of all were those faceless S.S. men still on the run who refused to give themselves up and who would try to pass themselves off as ordinary German civilians to the authorities fearing charges of war crimes being levelled against them. Some even wore disguises and posed as Poles or Norwegians. You needed eyes in the back of your head. Believe me one had to be on one's guard twenty four hours a day even in neutral Flensburg in those fact-finding days . . .

Speaking of men on the run, and all that anonymity stuff, I was then informed that it was indeed one of our very own Eleventh Armoured who had the honour of capturing the infamous William Joyce or "Lord Haw Haw", as he was better known to most of us. It appears that a member of the Tank Regiment had been sitting reading a book in one of Flensburg's lovely parks one Sunday morning when he heard a civilian speaking to some German kids who were playing there.

Only mildly interested at first seemingly, the soldier paid no attention but became intrigued when he noted how perfect the civilian's English was when he lapsed into it, after talking to the children in faultless German. He detected just a hint of an Irish accent. He then challenged him and asked him for his Passbuch or Passport which all German civilians were obliged to carry. At first it appears that Joyce tried to laugh it off. But then finally admitted that he was indeed William Joyce and surrendered quietly. So, yet another feather in the cap for the Eleventh Armoured.

But it was the S.S. on the loose who were the danger. That innocent looking German beside you in the main street gazing into that shop window could well be concealing a revolver on his person and be ready to use it. We had to be continually on our guard.

In fact for some weeks we were not allowed out on our own. We had to go about in pairs both armed. It may sound silly, even childish. But those measures were designed especially to keep us alive. One careless departure from that drill, one slight deviation could well nigh mean you saying goodbye to Flensburg and to life itself

Even more so since two of our outfit had been suddenly attacked and left for dead a few nights ago. A German police force had been hastily formed to keep an eye on the civilian population. But they too were suspect for a long time until they proved themselves. To be fair some of the civilians were quite affable, good-natured people on the whole, and welcomed our presence. Even more so when we pointed out to them where they could get a meal and probably a bed for the night. You got the impression that they too were equally glad it was all over.

Like I say, Flensburg seemed to have more than her fair share of beautiful frauleins and some of them knew it and could command a reasonable standard of living by attaching themselves to any British soldier of their choice, but again it was the officers who tried to hog the situation. They had a far bigger ration of compelling chocolates and cigarettes than any of the other ranks to barter with and believe you me they used that privilege to the utmost. And yet they were always the first to spout long and often to us about The "Non-Frat", an abbreviation for non fraternization.

That was the current phrase around then and it meant that no British soldier was allowed to fraternize for the foreseeable future with German citizens. Especially and most especially with the frauleins. Not that it was easy at any time, trying to get to grips with a fraulein legally or illegally since outside of barracks, soldiers had to be in pairs all the time in case of attacks on them by rogue S.S. men. Or even just run-of- the mill German deserters who just couldn't come to terms with defeat. Just imagine trying to do bit of canoodling with your mate looking on. Somehow it killed all the passion, don't you think?

The German night club we had commandeered and were using as a Naafi was going great guns with the troops. Business was booming. So much so that Paddy Mackin our sergeant decided we would have to have more civilian staff, to keep up with demands. Whilst we had no trouble recruiting men to work for us. For some reason or other the frauleins and the fraus just seemed somehow not to be interested. And we'd been opened fully three weeks without any requests for employment from any of the fairer sex.

And that was all the more surprising when you consider that the Naafi were offering free meals on top of wages. It may well be however that Flensburg was a victim of it's own prosperity. Having never been bombed they were short of very little in the way of food being as they were so near to neutral Denmark, the land of plenty. So Paddy decided to get tough and informed the appropriate authorities who immediately sent four young frauleins around the very next day to be interviewed by him with a view to working in the kitchen or as waitresses or even as general dogsbodies . . .

Anything less resembling general dogsbodies I'd yet to see when some frauleins were produced one day for our benefit. And then only after Paddy had appealed to the German authorities about the lack of response to his plea for female workers. I again was struck by the natural beauty of some of them when they were paraded in front of us for work that day. But it had to be said that those frauleins were less than enthusiastic about having to work for the British.

Paddy wasn't all that enthusiastic about interviewing them either. But I was. For I got lucky and was given the job of sitting in with him because of my slight knowledge of German. And after I got a good look at them I was more than glad I had been asked. As far as I was concerned It was like being asked to interview the Ziegfield Follies of '39. For they were an imposing bunch that lot.

First of all Paddy told me to ask them why they all looked so gloomy. Which I did in my best phrase-book German. I was answered curtly and to the point. " If we refuse to work for you British, our rations. They will be cut. Vot are we to do?" The very young fraulein with the golden hair was giving it to us straight. The ocean blue of those eyes of hers were tailor-made I thought to match that exquisite countenance and that flaxen hair. And she was looking for answers.

Answers I may say that neither myself nor Paddy either for that matter had any to offer. Paddy whispered furtively in my ear. "Ask her her name? The beautiful honey blonde one. She's obviously the spokesman for the other three." The other three weren't exactly of the ugly variety either I hasten to add. But the spectacular looking little blonde was dominating the whole proceedings. True. There were answers that the beautiful fraulein may not have been getting but there was no question about her ability, no question at all. I fumbled for my best German." Was ist ihre nahme?"

And again we got it straight back at us. "Meine nahme ist Johanne Marie Christiansen." I turned to Paddy, and shrugged my shoulders. "There you are, Paddy. That's her name but she's not giving any more than that away." Paddy still wasn't satisfied." Ask her where she lives. I'm sure I've seen her before?" Only in your dreams Paddy, I thought to myself, in your bloody dreams.

And I was equally certain that wasn't the reason for wanting to know where she lived. But he was the boss. So I persevered.

"Wo wohnen zie?" I asked our Marie. "Ich wohne auf der Wilhelmstrasse," she answered promptly with just a hint of a smile on those luscious lips that needed no lipstick whatsoever. Paddy was enjoying it but I myself didn't see myself as a kind of Gestapo merchant. But Paddy still wasn't happy. "Ask them if any of them are Nazis." I wasn't too sure about that one but anyway it didn't matter. For at this, our blonde example of resplendent beauty shouted over almost immediately. It was as though she was reading our lips. "Nein." she replied. Wir sind keine Nazis." I could hardly keep from laughing as I turned to Paddy. But I already knew what he was going to say. "The little bugger, must have read my lips. She'll take a bit of watching that one believe you me," he said shaking his head and grinning.

What next I wondered. Paddy was obviously impressed by my German if nothing else. He himself had been a regular soldier for ten years and had been in India for most of that time he'd told me. And he was used to himself telling flunkies and the likes what to do instead of the other way about. And he didn't know anything about the German language he confessed. Rightly or wrongly I got the impression that being Irish and having been in India for so long Paddy was having difficulty with the English language let alone the German. And this was going to be an entirely new experience for him, however puzzling.

"Now they're not Nazis, you say. Would they be waiters then, d'ye think?" Paddy had always been in the Army Catering Corps, and it must have been there that he got his promotion to sergeant. But to have made it to sergeant even in the Army Catering Corps, or to give it one of it's better acronyms. The A.C.C.C. Even allowing for the "Any Cunt Can Cook" interpretation of it all Paddy must have been one helluva good cook to have made it to sergeant.

We were getting nowhere fast. I shook my head. "Paddy," I said, "they're obviously not interested." But we went on. "But they've lost the war. They'll have to take a job or starve." But from where I was standing it didn't look that way and I told him so. "Paddy," I said, "you can only lose a war once, and I think they're well aware of that." "Now Eddie, don't be talkin' like that. Ask them civil like. If they would do a bit of waitin' on the tables in the Naafi and they'll maybe make a bit of money on tips and a few nice cakes to take home into the bargain . . . Go on, ask them nicely." Paddy had been just a little too long in India, I thought, to myself but I didn't have the heart to tell him. So I decided to try them out just one more time just for Paddy's sake.

I then explained at length as best I could that it would be very much to their advantage if they accepted our offer of a job in the Naafi. I stressed in particular that any goodies left over at night could be taken home by them after work. And that those cakes would be very well made by our sergeant and his other bakers. Would they at least think it over? They then went into a huddle and we were all eyes if not ears especially when they bent over, as they thrashed it out between them. Blondie still seemed to be the one to be convinced by the other three, and she appeared to be laying the law down by the look of things. After about five minutes they turned round and gave us the result of their deliberations. And again, guess what? Yes, It was Blondie who delivered the verdict.

And it was with bated breath, Paddy and myself listened to their verdict. Yes, they would work in our Naafi but since three of the other frauleins lived quite a distance out of town they would require transport home especially after dark. She, Blondie herself, wouldn't require transport home because she lived . . . She didn't have to finish the last sentence, because by this time even Paddy knew where she lived. "Where does she live, Paddy?" I shouted out smiling and pointing. It had even clicked with Paddy too.

"She lives in the Wilhelmstrasse," he cried, clapping his hands gleefully. And so accord was eventually reached and the girls promised to present themselves at the Naafi to be gainfully employed not by the British army but by the Naafi at Blondie's behest. Paddy agreed instantly with regards to the transport home. But I reckon if the frauleins especially Blondie had insisted on being flown back home in a helicopter, Paddy would have instantly acceded to her request.

All was well that ended well. So we could only wait and see if the girls turned out for work the following Monday. But they did. And there was a full house to see their debut in dealing with the tea, the wads and the chocolate eclairs. As to be expected, there were plenty of whistles, not to mention.a few cat-calls, from the troops. Blondie as usual was getting more than her fair share of the whistles and other remarks.

Then there was an incident when a member of the Tank Regiment tried to playfully knock off her Naafi-provided hat which she had perched cheekily on her blonde head. And only a timely intervention by Sergeant Paddy and myself prevented her planting a left hook on the rather taken aback trooper.

But as the weeks went by they gradually settled in and peace reigned for a while. Blondie still managed to fend off her admirers and did her job well. But she certainly took a bit of getting to know and there was a certain trooper waiting their turn to do just that. Then out of the blue she was promoted to an offshoot of The Naafi; The Gift Shop which, was only a few doors away. But as far as I was concerned it could well have been miles but gradually my patience was slowly beginning to pay off, and was almost on the point of getting that date. And I had a sneaking suspicion that the promotion of The Blonde Bombshell may well have been at Paddy's instigation.

Paddy denied that he had sent Blondie off to The Gift Shop . "Rubbish I'd be in there like a shot, but I'm too old. Now if I was only about ten years younger it would be a different matter." Somehow I believed him. Paddy couldn't tell a lie. He wouldn't know how to. He was an Indian\Irishman, after all. Seeing that there had been nothing sinister in Blondie's promotion I plucked up courage one night and went up the road and managed to stop her with out her landing one on me. After a few well-chosen words we retired to one of the many little cafe cum beer shops that were almost everywhere. I surprised even myself by holding down a conversation in German for about twenty minutes.

I even plucked up enough courage to ask her if I could call her Johanna; and to my total surprise she agreed. But I wasn't too sure how that was because her own command of the English language wasn't all that great. So I didn't want to read too much into it. But I did make some progress. Her number in The WilhelmStrasse was number four . . . So far so good. Next time she might even show me where the Wilhelmstrasse actually was . . .

But there was better to come, I finally coaxed her to go to the Cinema with me. My German was getting better. No, not Blondie. I mean my German lessons. I was getting really good at it and could hold a reasonable conversation that little bit better just above the phrase book standard and it was paying off. But after listening to Humphrey Bogart coming out with a mouthful of perfect German in the B movie we were watching I wasn't so sure. Then I realized that the film had been dubbed into English and I felt a little better. Then she led me to the Wilhelstrasse nummer vier. Number 4 Wilhelmstrasse was a builder's workshop with a large iron gate barring the way. Johanna then pointed to a building above.

Her father was a Foreman Plumber and as such had a house above the work-shops. We stood outside the gate for a while. It was just approaching ten o'clock and I noticed she kept looking at her watch. I asked her why and she told me that if she wasn't at the other side of that gate by ten oclock the key would be turned in the lock by papa. So when ten o'clock came I swiftly stole a kiss from those full soft lips. There was so much that I wanted to know about papa and the rest of her family. I wanted to know if her old man was a Nazi; not that I was all that bothered, as long as he didn't try to kill me. I wanted to know about her brothers. I knew she was the only girl in the family but the rest of the details would have to wait till another day. Papa was looming . . .

There were a lot of enquiries in the canteen where the honey blonde had gone but we decided to let them find out for themselves and some of them did. And some came seeking gifts in the gift shop but she wasn't having any and they soon got tired and withdrew to their canteen haunts again. It took me another week before I myself could approach her since she seemed to have attracted a lot of custom to the shop, and as she explained to me herself, she was very happy doing what she was doing working amongst nice things. She told me she wasn't interested in tea and cakes or even chocolate eclairs since her own mother made them herself for the Christiansen family.

So whether the move to the gift shop was by accident or design it most certainly didn't do my dating prospects with Johanna any harm at all. Because she agreed to let me accompany her to a charity concert that was to be held on Saturday in Flensburg's little opera house. So when Saturday came she showed me the two tickets that had been given to her by an air force pilot. I was taken aback at first.

"What kind of airforce pilot?" I asked, tongue-in cheek. "Luftwaffe or R.A.F.?" She took me seriously at first before it gradually dawned on her. "It was your own pilot." she said. "And what was an RAF pilot doing giving you tickets for a concert?" I asked, jokingly. Then she explained. And her English was getting better, no doubt about that. "He said he didn't vaunt zem for he voz goink home to England very early." I nodded solemnly. And if you think I was going to kid her about her accent or indeed her English, I didn't. I simply remembered what had nearly become of that soldier in the Tank Regiment, when he tried to knock her cap off that day.

She agreed to meet me at the door of the opera house that Saturday night at 7.p.m. as the concert was due to commence at 7.30. She was most meticulous about starting times. Was she as meticulous about other things I began to wonder. Or was it just that German obsession for detail. But all those surmises of mine were put to one side when she finally appeared bang on seven o'clock. She had a light white raincoat on as I remember for our first real date with a plain simple black frock underneath which only served to highlight her beauty. But then clothes somehow seemed an irrelevance as I got the impression that any adornment would always take second place. Stunning was a word I had never used much. Simply because I had never the occasion to use it. But now I had found one. There was no other word to describe her. That may sound a bit of an exaggeration. But that's as I saw her.

I expected at any minute for someone to come along and wave their hand over my eyes and say "Mc Cann. This is all a dream. You could never look at a woman like that. Correction, a woman like that would never look at you." And they would be right. Never at any time had any woman even remotely as beautiful as her ever looked at me before be it in England or in Scotland either for that matter . . .

Anything after the beautiful Johanna could only be rated as an anticlimax as far as I was concerned. She had done wonders for me for I had never felt better. And what's more I was gradually beginning to come to terms with myself and my nervous condition. For I was still under no illusions. I was well aware that I was no catch, being only about 5 feet four and a half inches tall at full stretch. But I did look after my appearance, and considered myself to be reasonably good looking. OK so maybe I did spruce myself up every chance I got. That may sound like conceit. But then again, it may well be that it was to compensate for my lack of height. So what. I was still old fashioned enough to think that there were other attributes that women looked for in men. And I was nailing my hopes firmly to that mast. So I made the most of every asset I had at my disposal. I was loyal and I had a good head of dark brown hair and no plukes or ugly looking spots that I was aware of. I also had a good strong set of white teeth which was another plus.

It may well be that taking emulsion on mother's orders saw to that. So even although I say it myself I wasn't a bad looking little fella. No bad breath either which couldn't be said for a lot of the women I used to meet at Barrowland's Ballroom on a Saturday night in Glasgow. I mean kissing or gum-sucking as we called it then should have been pleasant and at best a passionate pastime. But it wasn't, as far as I could remember

Instead, many after-dark embraces in those alleyways and narrow entrances to the back courts in Glasgow's Gallowgate were a disaster as far as I was concerned, something to be avoided at all costs. In those un-enlightened days, dental hygiene, to some women I'm sure, was something you used to scrub out a dentist's waiting room with. For believe you me, bad teeth and bad breath to match were the order of the day and nights up those alleys and closes when you were snogging. So bad was it then that it was known as *Halitosis Up the Closes.*
And I most certainly did not want to go racing back to those days ever again. A better option would be studying for the priesthood I reckoned . . .

After a night at the opera, ( No, not that, "A night at the Opera") things really took off. First of all she allowed me to call her by her shortened Christian name, "Hanni". Then a week or so later things really began to hot up. After a suitable dalliance outside the iron gates of Wilhelmstrasse 4 a window from upstairs in the house opened and a head stuck was stuck out. It could have been her mother's. It so happened that it was. She beckoned for us to come up. And it was approaching the witching hour of ten. So far so good McCann I thought, and upstairs we went . . .

What struck me when we entered the house was the pleasant heat that was being generated through the house by the means of small stove-like fires with little glass doors which showed what looked like little pieces of coal burning merrily inside. What ever it was that was burning inside those little stove things, it worked. It was the first time I had ever seen anything like that before. The nearest being the usual big ones in those nissen huts that we were billeted in in Britain. But the heat wasn't convected nearly as well as it was in there.

Even at home in Glasgow I remember my parents moving into a brand new council house in Carntyne, round about 1932, a four appartment house no less, with a living room that had a fire which burned ordinary coal. And from what I could remember it heated only those who were in the living room. Even then it warmed only those who were sitting right up against it. The heat was not convected anywhere else. The bedrooms had a plain simple gas mantled-type fire which not only didn't heat anyone but was smelly and inefficient to boot, as my brothers and sisters would readily confirm having shivered many a winter cursing the coldness with me. That's why I was so taken with the simplicity of all the heat coming out from those small stoves in the Wilhelmstrasse.

Her mother, a really small homely type of woman made me immediately welcome and shook my hand. Then papa emerged from another room, bowed his head slightly and shook my hand. I thought at first that it may well have been a note of subserviance to us victors but as usual I was wrong. I learned later that this slight nod was one of politeness accompanied by a "Malzeit" which in that part of Schleswig Holstein meant the equivalent of the Americans "Have a nice day".

We then sat down to a meal which was usually eaten around seven or eight of an evening but which in this particular case had been delayed for my benefit. It was "abendbröt;" the German name for supper. It was a delightful meal consisting of three kinds of bread, white, brown and black; the latter containing an ingredient which I had never heard of before; "pumpernickel" I was later told that it was, with some sort of wheat germ that gave bread a unique flavour. And it certainly worked for me.

Together with this assortment of bread we had tomatoes, cheese and some hard-boiled eggs and fried potatoes. Sumptious was the only word to really describe it.

Not unlike what we used to know in the sixties and seventies in Glasgow, as a "high tea". And all this in 1945 too in a country that had lost the war. And in an odd sort of way that heartened me a great deal because it endeared me still more to those other losers, Celtic. Maybe, just maybe there was still a chance for them yet, and for me too! . . .

After the meal Hanni's father showed me around the house. It was a modest dwelling by any standards. I was still impressed by the heating process. He said it was very simple. But it wasn't to me. I was also introduced to tobacco plants for the first time in my career. Up in the loft there were plants which he said he grew for his own use. Then when they had reached a certain maturity he brought them indoors. They would then be taken up to the loft where they were watered, brushed and tended, with loving care daily. Because he was an avid smoker as were most of the Germans; although he didn't like commercial types of tobacco like Capstan, Players, or even Senior Service, which was my own particular favourite at that time. Nor did Hanni smoke in those early days. The smoking unfortunately came later.

The following evening I was shown round their allotment which took it's place amongst many others about two kilometres out of town. And believe you me potatoes and vegetables proliferated there together with chickens and pigs. Self sufficiency, was obviously the name of the game in Flensburg in those days. I was even invited to watch the sacrificial pig being slaughtered in order to feed quite a few families. Nothing was wasted. Even the blood was utilized in many ways to make black puddings, of all things. The parable about the loaves and the fishes was a simile that sprang to mind on that particular occasion. And whilst it would never figure high on my list as a spectator sport it was very interesting for all that. And it should be remembered that these people had to live and survive by dint of hard work, coupled with a big slice of what I thought was ingenuity. And each one had his or her own particular way of doing those day to day things as they evolved.

As time went on our romance blossomed. We took time off whenever we could to go picnicking in Glücksburg where Hanni was born and where the family had previously lived before papa made that short journey to neighbouring Flensburg to take up his post as a foreman plumber in the Wilhelmstrasse. Glücksburg was a delightful spot with long stretches of sandy beaches which we often retired to, weather permitting. And there we would just lie and soak it all up.

Sometimes; just sometimes we would be lying there with our arms around each other, when on looking up I would be aware of eyes being trained on us by others on that beach. Could that be an ex S.S. soldier further along the beach staring balefully at the two of us I would wonder. Was that one-armed civilian sitting beside a woman and child, about to come up and confront me? Or even try to gun us down as we lay there. They didn't need to see me wrapped in a Union Jack flag to know exactly who and what I was. They knew instinctively. Or maybe he that soldier or sailor was just dwelling on how it all had gone dreadfully wrong for him and his family as he surveyed his damaged body and the loss of that arm or leg. It proved once again that the war wasn't over entirely for some people. Then again it could all have been an over-reaction to a very delicate situation. There, but for the grace of God . . . and all that sort of stuff. Whatever it was, it was decidedly off-putting, not to mention, uncomfortable. And whatever else it did, it would teach you to pick your friends, and your enemies, with the utmost care.

For there were still a lot of angry, ruthless men out there with very little to lose. Not all of them, it has to be said, had given their all of their own volition. For with my knowledge of the language I had managed to penetrate some of those minds of theirs. And one would have had to have been inhuman despite all that had gone before, not to have felt a little sorry for that minority and their present plight.

Hanni's oldest brother Willi was also a prisoner-of-war captured by the Russians and she was very conscious of this. Even to this very day they never knew if he was alive or dead. Nothing was ever heard of him, another brother Heinz at that time was a prisoner-of-war in America. So it wasn't all one-sided stuff. The youngest of her brothers Friederich was disabled, otherwise he too would have had to do his bit. The diplomat in me made me steer clear of Adolf's attitude to conscientious objectors . . .

But things had gone on apace in Flensburg, because the frauleins were causing all sorts of distractions to the troops. Some soldiers were even refusing to go on leave. Many of them didn't want to go back to their wives or to their sweethearts or whoever was waiting for them over there. It wasn't all the troops who were affected in this way. Just those who were lucky enough like myself to land on our feet, so to speak, in the land of plenty which shouldn't have been a land of plenty but was. And that place was Schleswig Holstein and the town was Flensburg.

The fraulein situation was in danger of becoming a Diplomatic Incident. And even warranted questions being asked in the House of Commons. If the House of Commons was still sitting that is. For example what did a commanding officer say to a wife or a sweetheart demanding to know why her husband or boy friend wasn't getting leave when in fact he was. But just wasn't taking it. And what sort of reason was one going to offer them for their non-acceptance.

In the cold light of day it was very clear. Very clear indeed. In Flensburg, what they wanted was there. Not over there. It was in Deutschland. Going Back to Britain even for a short time and that, to quote a well- known joke was what they were holding back for. But it wasn't just a case of deserting their loved ones. It was the going back to Britain bit that jarred. It meant not only going back to the wives or the sweethearts. It meant going back to a country who although acknowledged winners of a war were in danger of losing out on everything else.

Being a Yank was different. Although they too had a few defectors they were still going back to a hero's welcome. Back to a country that war or no war had wanted for nothing. Back to a country and a land of milk and honey. Yet to a land who was only too pleased to turn those biblical but out-dated goodies into something more tangible like free housing and land to own. And war pensions to boot . . . They were going back to a land that made them "a veteran" even if they only served a week in the trenches. Back to a land that draped flags all over their backyard. So glad to see them back. And not only that but they gave you a chest full of medals into the bargain, even though you didn't exactly prise that lugar out of the enemy's grasp with your own bare hands. That's what they were going back to. They had it all ways! *Both at Home and Away!*

And what *were we* going back to? We would be going back to sitting in front of a tribunal to fight for a pension. To have no rights to a council house even if you'd done five years or so away fighting. Back to a country that was still giving you an ounce of butter for your tea. We would be going back to a country that told you that you had no special favours. Back to a country which even if you had won an award for bravery, or even for outstanding gallantry, wouldn't even try to find you, or have the decency to even tell you you'd won such an award. For that's what going back entailed.

Nor would they even want to know if you were still alive to receive that money. And no, it wouldn't just be for that measly ten quid that was rightfully yours for getting the M.M. or the twenty quid if it was for the V.C. And never you mind if we advertised it or not. It was for none of those reasons. If you don't claim it, you won't get it. And if you do get a pension old chap for a war disability, we' ll keep an eye on you and haul you back here to see if you've got better from your war wounds. And if you have jolly well improved a little, we'll jolly well take it away from you again. So there, that's what you would be going back to. You would not be going back to a country fit for heroes, you would just be going back to a country to try to survive in and nothing more . . . !

## Chapter Seven

*A Mother's Plea And Resistance Thereto*

Whilst I couldn't speak for the rest I myself most certainly had no intention of rushing home to Glasgow from Flensburg despite the entreaties of my mother to do just that. I had one brother Charlie who was still in the army. He was in the Seaforth Highlanders and due to be demobbed soon. Why couldn't I just do the same? My oldest brother Johnnie was already demobbed from the R.A.F. Then there was Tommy or Tam as he was better known. Poor Tam if he had been alive today would surely have made the *Guinness Book of Records* for he was one of the last to join up but one of the first to get out of the army. And only then I'm sure because he was drunk at the time. Someone seemingly stuck a form in front of him and held his hand whilst he signed on. He was in the Royal Army Service Corps for about three months. And although having had bronchitis since ever any of us could remember, he somehow managed to get through the medical.

He had a strong liking for the hard stuff. And somehow it managed to tolerate him too. They both got along well. In the three months he was in the army he managed to make it to sergeant; caught bronchitis again, the same one I think and was invalided out with a thirty per cent war pension. One of the few to beat the system and ironically for contracting bronchitis whilst in the Armed Forces. That was Tam who could do anything and drive anything, and fix anything, until it came down to fixing himself.

Good old Tam, I could have told my mother that he was another reason for not coming home as could my brother Charlie. Tam was my mother's favourite if somewhat wayward son. She always had a special place in her heart for him, because his wife had died in childbirth whilst having their daughter Frances a year or so before the war. Then as was the custom Tam came to live with us now that we had moved up in the world to a bigger council house in Carntyne.

We were all then more or less left with the task of bringing up baby Frances which was something that would most certainly have been more difficult had we still been in our old home in Stevenson Street in Glasgow's Calton for Tam was still mourning the loss of his wife. Once again he became more and more involved with that very good friend of his of long standing; "John Barleycorn."

That was when the rituals began most evenings for Charlie and myself. The order would emanate from my mother shouting from her bed for us to go down the hall to Tam's bedroom and to ensure he didn't burn himself to death together with the bedclothes. Which would be the greater loss a thoroughly browned off Charlie and I would often cruelly sometimes wonder, for another of Tam's hobbies was smoking in bed. Most especially when he was drunk. And that was nightly. The moment he got into bed the fags would come out. And for hours on end he would sit up in bed smoking, coughing and spluttering. Often, whenever Charlie or I thought Tam was about to take his final puff and doze off one of us knowingly on cue would prise the still-lit fag from his fingers. It was a knowledge that could only be acquired from being "on call" night after night after night.

But despite our experiences on "the Tam Watch" which Charlie and I called it, there were times when we got it wrong. Sometimes Tam, on the point of dropping off into a deep sleep, would suddenly decide to fight it, sit up and demand one more fag before going to sleep. The whole rigmarole would then start all over again. As a matter of fact all things considered, we may well have been a minority, but Charlie and I were certainly glad the war came along. At least there was always a chance of us getting a good night's sleep.

So with Tam still at home I wasn't prepared to risk all those night watches again, even more so now due to my own nervous state. Because believe you me our Tam was fearless and would probably expect me to be able to do all the things he could do. I don't think he had a nervous bone in his body, and anyway Charlie was due to marry soon and with only my three sisters at home that would have left me as the only domiciled male. There was my father too of course who never at any time saw eye to eye with Tam and that was putting it mildly. So that left little old me and I honestly couldn't see myself doing the bedside manner thing again whenever Tam was in his cups.

I could well understand my mother's insistence on my coming home but I was determined not to be swayed. My mother was a physically strong woman and would manage to survive without me. Or it may well have been because I was the youngest of the family. Or perhaps she had read in the papers how a lot of British soldiers were falling for those femmes fatale, or the German equivalent thereof, and didn't want me to fall into that same category. But I was already in that category whether she liked it or not and was infinitely pleased to be there. Now that the war was over news was scarce. So there had to be something else for people to read about. Consequently, the press went to town about the British troops, and those frauleins and believe me they went about it in a big way.

"German Frauleins Ensnaring Our Soldiers," was one headline. "German Frauleins Are Home-Wreckers," shrieked another. The papers were right to a certain extent. British soldiers were deferring their demobilization for up to a year. The War Office was being bombarded for permission to marry their German sweethearts. And at first the War Office refused to countenance their requests.

Especially to those soldiers who were already married in Britain. But I wasn't married. And I had already made my mind up that I would stay in Flensburg if need be; if my request to marry the girl of my choice was turned down.

I had already weighed up the pros and cons of staying on in Germany; in Flensburg in particular the ban remained. What would I be missing? I examined my conscience. Just what would I miss most in not going back to Glasgow? First of all I would miss my family I suppose to a certain extent. I could perhaps force myself not to miss watching Celtic try to play football every Saturday. I would miss those hot pies with those delicious hot peas on top. I would always lament the loss of not being able to buy a quarter of Liquorice Allsorts or a couple of pieces of Puff Candy. But after a lot of deep thought I figured that would be about all I would miss. And sleep of course if Tam was still around . . .

And what wouldn't I miss? First on my list would be not having to hang around the gates of Sir William Arrols; or Beardmore's at my father's behest every morning just as I'd done ever since I left school. Those most certainly I would not miss. Because to secure an apprenticeship then in the steel works was the ultimate in my father's opinion And still was, whereas in my humble opinion, I considered it to be the first rung on the ladder to ultimate obscurity. My father would have killed me if he'd known that on many occasions in the early days I didn't go near those non-pearly gates of those steel yards. Even on the odd occasion when I did venture near enough to ask I would hope and pray that there would be no vacancies available. I would then report back to my father looking suitably dejected when really all I wanted to do was to sing like Bing Crosby.

I most certainly would not miss oxo cubes. (For like Smithy I could still smell those dead cows in Normandy.) Nor would I miss green smelly cabbage and spam fritters. And I would most definitely not miss that Christmas goose which was despatched to us religiously every year from Ireland; especially in those earlier years. Even now I often wonder and believe me my heart went out to that postman of ours if indeed he was still around, which on reflection I very much doubt. For if truth be told it's quite possible we hastened his demise. Because no one, and I mean no one could have withstood those Goosey Goosey Christmas Deliveries to the McCanns at 295 Stevenson Street, Glasgow without suffering some grievous after-effects.

I always got the impression that the whole of the East End of Glasgow was alerted to the aforesaid McCann Delivery round about the festive season bearing in mind that postal deliverys from Ireland in those days took about seven days; sometimes more. So that in many cases that trussed-up goose, feathers and all; as it was in life, would be well on it's way to Glasgow, and more important still also well on it's way to decomposition, like I say seven days was normal delivery time for Irish parcels. Imagine then if you dared the state of that bird never mind the state of the postman and his sense of smell when it reached the McCanns in the close two stairs up in 295 Stevenson Street Calton Glasgow E.1. They reckoned that one time the smell was even detected in Gallowgate; about a quarter of a mile away. And they do say that one Christmas there was talk, just talk mind you of them actually evacuating Stevenson Street temporarily till well after Christmas and well into the New Year . . .

Nostalgia. Nostalgia. But there was no going back for me much as I loved my native city of Glasgow. I would certainly miss those long walks along Argyle Street on a Saturday. I would certainly miss the buzz that was forever around Buchanan Street and Sauchiehall Street. I would miss all those things. But I could learn to live without them. I would miss too the Glasgow characters; the patter in the pubs after a game at Celtic Park. And those street theatres where a Charlie Chaplin lookalike without any trace of nerves would put down a little pallet on the edge of pavement and do an impersonation of Charlie's walks and dance routines down to the very last detail. He would even do the twirly bit with that famous walking stick and then come round with the hat. Only Glasgow could come up with those characters in those early days when I was young. Those I would miss!

But then came a dramatic about turn in events in Germany. The War Office caved in over the fraulein situation. Allied forces could apply to marry their German sweethearts if they so wished. But those same frauleins would require to undergo a medical examination and they would be vetted to see if they belonged to any subversive organisation such as the National Socialist Party in which case they would not be granted a visa.

They certainly didn't intend to make it easy for any us who were involved with a fraulein and there were thousands, demanding full rights for their intended future wives. I myself deferred for another year because I really was enjoying life for once in my entire life. So why should I give it all up for an uncertain future in an uncertain world in Civvy Street? I had no special skills apart for my stint as a touch-typist. Whereas here in Flensburg I was with the girl I loved and I could teach her English which she was desperate to learn and which she had a natural aptitude for and was learning rapidly. Not only that but I was my own boss, more or less because Paddy had succumbed to his wife's threats and took his demob. For Paddy it was either fall for the lure of the fraulein or risk the ire of Bridget. So there being no more options around, Paddy chose the latter.

Hanni and I spent most of my last year doing the things normal couples do. We made love. We picnicked in Glücksburg; particularly in a lovely spot we luckily discovered later on which was aptly called "Solitude". And we enjoyed ourselves to the full despite everything else bad that was happening elsewhere. We also became part of a transitional period when the Norwegians took over the role of peacekeepers as our own troops gradually got fewer and fewer due todemobilisation and other postings.

I applied for a visa for Hanni, who by then was expecting our child. I even went back to the Catholic church I'd first went to on coming to Flensburg for the first time. And it was there at Mass one Sunday morning that I first saw this German priest. It had been my intention to ask his advice about myself and my German sweetheart but after watching him all through the Mass I decided against it. For he was arrogance personified that little rotund German cleric. No standing in the pulpit for him. He literally marched sometimes backwards, up and down the aisles, with fists clenched, as he preached. And I got the impression that he wouldn't be averse to lashing out at some of the congregation if the opportunity ever arose. He was obviously straight out of the Hitler mould.

But the little militant priest was no longer there, which was maybe just as well Because I had changed my mind about getting married in Flensburg after all. There was too much red tape around at that time and too many taboos. So I decided that Hanni and our child would come to Scotland whenever permission for them to travel was granted. I would go home first when my year's deferment was up and await their arrival over in Britain which I sincerely hoped would not be too long in coming

My own command of the German language was coming along leaps and bounds and Hanni's English was also improving rapidly. I always remembered my French teacher at school telling me that no matter how good you thought you were nothing could compare with the conversational aspect. And how true that was. So whenever I had some time on my hands I would go into one of those many coffee shops and cafes that abounded in Flensburg, buy a coffee, and on occasions buy a cigar and just listen. If I was spoken to in German I would respond in German as best I could and more often than not I would get a nod of assent. This told me that I was being understood and that pleased me no end.

I loved going "underground" like that and did it often even in France and Belgium. I just liked languages and welcomed the challenge to converse with people in their own tongue. And this gave me a great opportunity to try and understand the German people. Whenever the occasion arose I would try and find out the thoughts of Hanni's father with regards to the rise of Hitler and the ensuing consequences of his "Coming". I hoped that I would get an honest answer from him having taken him to be a level headed sort of man who wouldn't be easily swayed. So I managed to get him alone one night when Hanni and her mother were out.

He poured me out a glass of schnapps. I then asked one of the many questions I'd been dying to ask him for a long time. "Tell me," I asked," is it true that if you didn't say "Heil Hitler" and give that salute with the right hand raised you could be jailed or even worse? " Willi Christiansen put his glass down and smiled over at me and shook his head. "I am not saying a lot of them didn't like it when you didn't give the salute or say Heil Hitler every minute of the day but no." His smile got even broader. And he was not a man given to smiling a lot at any time "No, no, there would be no putting in jail. Some of my work comrades who liked Hitler and what he was doing perhaps would not talk to me for a while if I did not respond or agree with them but that was all. There would be no shooting. There were many more people than you think who did not like Hitler and what he was doing . . . "

"And you yourself. What did you think of Hitler?" I asked. He shrugged his shoulders. "There were a lot of good things he did for Germany. He brought work to Germany. He built many houses and schools." "Any other good things he did?" "Oh yes, he taught us how to provide for ourselves with regards to food and things. He taught us that nothing should be wasted. That there was a use for almost everything no matter how useless it may look. He encouraged everyone to grow their own food in case of emergencies." "Was there anything else good that he taught you?" "Oh yes. He told us that we had to fear no one and that we would be once more a strong nation." "And you believed him?" "Of course. Why should we not believe him. He was our leader. And we could see such good progress we were making under his leadership."

" But did you like Hitler himself as a man?" I persisted. He shrugged his shoulders again. "As a man what did I know? It did not worry me that much. I had my family. My wife, my daughter and three sons. I am a simple man. I work for my family and I wish to be left alone. If he left me alone to work at my work I should not worry what kind of man he was."

" What did you think of his attitude to the Jews?" I asked. "Did you agree with him there?" "If you are talking about these death camps which the newspapers say he constructed to gas them and kill them along with women and children. No. I would say that he was very wrong. I do not hate anyone enough to kill them in such a horrible way. To me all people have an equal chance to live." Fair enough I thought then went on further. For I wanted to know.

"Did you like Jews?" I asked. He shrugged his shoulders. "Did you know any Jewish people?" He nodded his head. "Of course I knew some Jews. We bought all our Christmas presents and jewellery from their shops in the Grosse Strasse." "And did you speak much to them?" "Of course. Why should I not speak with them?" "Did you have any Jewish friends?" He thought for a moment then shook his head. "No. I did not have any Jewish friends." "And why didn't you?" I asked. "Because in Flensburg here we do not have many Jewish people. And anyway they are business people who do business. I am only a man who works. Socially we are very different. I shall bet you do not have many Jewish friends either. Do you?" I thought hard and fast and tried to come up with one Jewish name that I could call a friend. But I had to admit defeat.

"What do you think Hitler had against the Jewish people?" His brow furrowed a little at this. "I think maybe he thought they possessed too much of Germany's money. Because they did not work hard enough for it. They did not do what you call . . . " he faltered here so I thought I'd help him out. "You mean they did not do any manual work like building houses or working in the fields?" He nodded assent." You have Jews in England and Scotland. No?" "Yes we do. But we don't put them in concentration camps or put them to death like Hitler did!"

He shrugged his shoulders and shook his head vigorously "No, that was very wrong in my mind if that is true. People are people. It does not matter what religion you are or what country you are from, you are a people of God. And that is why I did not like what Hitler did to the Jewish people. For them I am very sad."

"What would have been your solution to the Jews possessing all of Germany's finances?" He thought hard and fast again and poured me, and himself another schnapps before replying. "I am not a political man. But I would have asked them to contribute more of their money to the German people to help create work and industry. And I am sure that more of the Jewish people would have been willing to help the German government. But they did not have a chance. They were not even asked."

I believed this man and not just because I wanted to marry his daughter. Indeed he was the main stumbling block earlier on to our getting together. It was just that he appeared to speak from the heart. And I was also glad that he was not a big man. He was slightly built with a rather thin face. He most certainly did not look "Master Race" material. I would even go as far as to say that he was the perfect antithesis to any type of bullying whatsoever.

At first his main argument against his daughter forming an association with me was that he thought she would receive special favours from myself and from the Naafi in particular to the detriment of other people. And I'm sure he meant every word of what he said. And it wasn't just that they had possibly a better standard of life than most. However I managed to talk him round. He was an independent type of man and from what I could gather he was a proud man. But Hanni assured me that he could at times be very outspoken and that's possibly the reason he didn't go overboard about Hitler and his cohorts.

Later that night when Hanni and her mother returned we had supper or abendbröt with the usual mixture of goodies again. There were tiny little potatoes which had been boiled then fried. They very nice and very tasty. I was then invited down to their cellar in the basement to see what was virtually a cold store crammed full with jars and jars of gherkins, and onions, peas and beans. Every type of vegetable imaginable was there neatly labelled and dated. Pickled pork. Pickled beef. Black pudding too. All ready for the table. This was The Good Life indeed. I could only hope that it all augured well for the future of my wife whenever she received permission to come over to the U.K. and marry me.

It was now time for me to go back to Scotland and to await the arrival of my sweetheart. There was nothing to fear now, not a cloud in the sky, not one single thing to stop us from being married in Scotland. I could not have been happier. My health was improving by the minute. My nerves were getting steadier. Johanna was the best thing that had ever happened to me and I put it all down to my meeting her. All it would take to make the future complete would be for Smithy Pricey and young Sonny to walk into that Flensburg Naafi and slap me on the back. But there was an old but very true saying that : "You can't have everything."

It was then that I decided to go down and say my goodbyes to some of the boys who had taken over from us in the Naafi. I ordered a beer which I was told was on the house seeing I was leaving and was about to take my first sip when I felt someone tap me on the shoulder. "McCann. Eddie McCann?" I looked round and nodded. "Can I sit down?" "Sure" I said. "Why not? It's a free country."

I then saw that he was a sergeant in the 3rd Tank Regiment. "I hope you don't mind," he said as he sat down opposite me with his pint. "But I've got some news for you. It's not very good news I'm afraid but I thought it only right that you should hear it first from the right source." He took off his black beret from his head and laid it on the table. Things were beginning to look ominous. "O.K. Are you ready for this?"

My head was beginning to get lighter again. Something it hadn't done for ages; that in itself was not a good sign. I knew then that he was going to tell me something I didn't want to hear like, All leave had been stopped? No more frauleins were being allowed to leave Germany? The Military Government had stepped in and had put a stop to it? I wasn't quite sure now if I wanted to hear what that smug looking sergeant opposite me with his pint of beer had to say so I decided to pre-empt him. "They've cancelled all l-leave, haven't they?" I gulped. He shook his head. "Then they've stopped us marrying the frauleins?" Again he shook his head " No ban on marrying frauleins?" He closed his eyes and went silent for a second. "Then what's so bloody important?" I snapped.

"Look, you were in the 11th Armoured the same as me weren't you?" he said, putting his two hands in front of himself as though to calm me down. "Yes I was." I said. "Overloon?" He nodded his head. "Me too," he said slowly and a little sadly. "That's the bad news I was meaning." He hesitated then went on again slowly. "You were with that Vickers machine gun outfit weren't you?" I nodded my head again. Somehow I was beginning not to like this guy whatever it was he had come to tell me.

"That field beside the railway line. Pelting with rain, remember? Hemmed in. Snipers all over the place!" My eyes closed and I was trying to keep that tripod leg steady again in my head . . . " That carrier of yours was blown away mate. And the entire crew copped it. I'm sorry to have to tell you this. But there was some bum information given out some time ago about who came through it and who didn't. And I was told by some of the lads that you were in one of those carriers that had a Vickers mounted on it. Is that right?" I didn't reply. I couldn't reply. I could only keep my eyes closed. Who was this bastard? And why was he telling me all these things now? Suddenly I didn't want to hear any more from this man. Who did he think he was talking to? I stood up, "What are you on about?" I hissed, "I saw the bloody lists myself with my own eyes. None of their names were on that list!" The sergeant's brow furrowed. "What lists?" he asked, puzzled. "Nobody issues lists of soldiers dead or otherwise during conflict. You should know that you must have dreamt it!" My head was buzzing again like that day on that train outside Hamburg but it was no dream. No!

What was he saying? That I was lying about those lists I had seen with my own eyes? He beckoned me to sit down. "Calm down. Calm down." He looked over at me fixedly. "I don't know what lists you're talking about. Anyway, it's my fault. I had forgotten that you were wounded out with a severe head wound and I'm very sorry for putting you in such a state. I should have known better. Let's just forget about any lists. That's not why I wanted to see you."

He began to look at me more fixedly than ever and his voice took on a more measured tone. "I just happened to hear that you had been asking around about some of your mates. Right?"

I nodded and sat down. "You're saying there were no lists. There were no names?" He shook his head. "No. Most certainly were not." I closed my eyes. I wanted the bastard to be wrong but he sounded as though he knew something I didn't. "Look pal," he went on, "I'm dreadfully sorry to have to tell you this but all three occupants of that carrier of yours were killed outright. They never stood a chance." I tried to keep my voice steady. "And how is that you know so much about it all?" I asked. The sergeant looked me straight in the eyes. " Because I was there. That's why. We had just been ordered forward when that eighty-eight came over. It missed us and hit your carrier. And if you hadn't been lying across that carrier you'd have copped it too. I'm sorry to have to tell you but you're as well knowing the truth."

"And h-how do you know so much about our carrier. And about me lying across the top?" He smiled wanly. "We were right behind your carrier and we knew you were in trouble. We could see you struggling with that tripod when the flares went up. But there was not a lot we could do. All I know is that if you hadn't been lying across that carrier you would have been dead too, I'm afraid. The blast catapulted you out of the carrier. Right?"

I didn't answer. Nor did I want to. I didn't want to do anything. It was over. The little fragile world that I was trying to re-build for myself was now in tatters. Pricey, Smithy and young Sonny were all dead according to this sergeant. Nothing mattered now. Three of my best friends had been blown to smithereens, if this cunt had to be believed. I didn't want to believe him. But he seemed to know all the details about the squad.

It just wasn't fair. It just wasn't bloody fair. Suddenly I didn't want to know anything any more. Or anyone . . . I wasn't even sure if I wanted to know my sweetheart any more. Her countrymen had destroyed the only real mates I had ever known. They had killed them. We'd all trained for two solid years together. And for what . . . ?

" I'm so sorry. But I thought you had the right to know. I'd heard that you'd been enquiring about them from some of the lads. And another reason was that a few weeks ago there were some rumours going around about who had got out of Overloon and who hadn't. Did you know that?" Yes, "I said." And their names weren't on those lists." He shook his head again "That's because there weren't any lists.

You've got to believe that. I only came here to put you in the picture and to prevent you getting your hopes up. Believe me I'm very sorry. I just thought you had that right. I didn't want you to still think that they were all still alive, most especially you . . . I'm so very very sorry." He patted my shoulder and got up from his seat. "Oh, and by the way, don't think you're alone. I lost a lot of mates there too you know. The bastards almost massacred us. Anyway. Good luck!" And with that he was gone and my own little world with him. Now I knew why those bloody gongs had been handed out. They had to give them to somebody. Didn't they? That was probably why that sergeant got the V.C. and I got that second prize . . . Bastards . . . !

I sat and cried for about ten minutes. The three of them should have been sitting there having a beer with me. Instead of that they were all gone. I didn't know quite what to do next. There didn't seem to be any point to anything any more. I wondered where they'd be buried? Probably in some cemetery in Overloon. Bloody Bloody Overloon. I finished my free beer and swore to myself that I would be very wary indeed of ever getting anything free again. I unburdened myself to Johanna that night before I left because she saw straight away that something was troubling me. She listened in silence. "If you do not want me to come to Scotland Eddie I will not come if it is too painful." She then told me how her oldest brother Willi had been in Russian hands for about three years nor was there any news to say whether he was dead or alive. They had been told absolutely nothing. Maybe I was being too harsh all around, too hard to everyone, to Smithy and the lot. Even to my very own little sweetheart. It was then I asked Johanna if she still wanted to come to Scotland to marry me. And she gave me her answer with a very loving kiss and a hug and tears which fortunately for me were all the assurances I needed.

But it was still with a heavy heart that I took my temporary leave of Flensburg. For it was time go back to Scotland and face the music and there would be music to face all right together with some equally difficult lyrics to go with that music I reckoned. For not only was I breaking the mould, I was burgling the factory that made the moulds so to speak and troubled times lay ahead.

And that latest bit of grim news I'd received about poor Smithy and company had reduced me somewhat already. But I would just have to get on with my life and I just hated goodbyes. It was as simple as that. For as a child I used to have to travel to Ireland during the school holidays with my parents and brothers and sisters. Now the distance between Scotland and Ireland have never varied geographically as we all know, but in the early 1930s it took fully two days to get there and two days to get back.

And oh how I dreaded those farewells at those old broken down railway stations in the Free State of Ireland. First my uncle would drive us there in the pony and cart from the farm which took over an hour. Then there would be tears flooding down our faces as we raised cheeks up to be kissed and cuddled by our uncle, our aunt and our cousins. All that because we were going on a train then a boat. Then it was on to another train. It was as though we were going to the other side of the world never to be seen again. When in fact we were only going on a journey which today would take no more than an hour or so on a plane. But even in planes I still hated those goodbyes.

And now I was going back to Blighty myself to face my own critics. Deep down I knew my own wedding plans would not go down well with my mother and father. Especially with my mother. Apart from my fiancée not being British, Irish, or even Scottish, she was not a Catholic and that in her book made her unacceptable. The mere fact that she was German was of no consequence I didn't think. And expecting a child out of wedlock would be even more unacceptable. But it was one of the many things I would have to contend with. I just hoped and prayed that I had recovered both physically and mentally enough to enable me to cope. I felt more confident within myself. But it was only now that I was beginning to put things behind me; something which I should have done long ago.

Even before I took my temporary leave of my future wife in Flensburg my father was still writing to tell me about how my local newspaper had made me front page news over my award of the M.M. That pleased me. I only hoped that they would be equally generous when I brought my German wife home to live in Britain. Not that I was alone in falling in love with a fraulein. I didn't know the exact figure of frauleins who were to marry in Britain. But I did know it was a substantial number. I knew that by marrying Hanni I wouldn't have been the most popular of men. But that's how it was. Then again she wouldn't be the only fraulein in Scotland. Strength in numbers? Only time would tell.

All eyes would be upon us. No question about that. Would they settle down to their new environment in Great Britain? Deep down I was glad I was not alone in my quest and that we would all be given a chance to make our intended marriages work. I certainly had every intention my making new venture work. And one of the first things I would be doing when I got home would be looking for a decent job. Because as far as I was concerned I most certainly did not intend to take the first dead end job that came along. Nor even the second one come to that.

And so I sailed away into the sunset to Blighty and then to Scotland. I didn't know quite what to expect when I got there but somehow I felt ready for them.

I knew exactly what I wanted to do. I wanted to renew acquaintance with my father and mother and my brothers and sisters first of all. Just to let them know that I hadn't grown two heads since they'd seen me last. They knew of course about my association with my German fraulein. Even although the news had reached there I wasn't sure if it had quite made it to the front page of our local paper. But I could well imagine the kind of conversations that would be taking place in Carntyne, even as I wrote home.

" Just imagine. Wee Eddie McCann, him that was in the Argylls. That's right, him that sang with Jack Hylton's band that week in the Empire just before the war. He won that talent contest and sang with the band for a week when they were in Glasgow. I wasn't there but they say he was very good. He sang 'Stardust.' And they were right. I did sing 'Stardust' in Glasgow's Moss's Empire, in early 1939. And I've still got the telegram to prove it, to this very day. And I beat off a lot of stiff competition to do it even if I say so myself. The queues for the auditions stretched along Sauchiehall Street then down West Nile Street.

And what a thrill that was for me to do just that. Beating all that opposition for the chance to sing with one of the biggest and most famous bands in Britain, was something I shall never forget till the day I die. I remember too chatting to Jack Hylton's resident singer back stage after the performance and he told me that if I went down to London I couldn't fail to become a resident crooner with one of the other big bands like Roy Fox, Lou Praeger, and even Joe Loss and his famous orchestra. He reckoned I couldn't fail but to make it big down there.

But did I get the chance to go down to London? Not on your life! My father wouldn't hear of it. Yes you guessed it. Next morning I was doing my usual stint of hanging round the gates of the Beardmore's the Sir William Arrols and the rest. And deep down that's one thing I shall never forgive my father for. Then again some may say I should have taken that chance myself and cut myself off. And I should have. I should have made a stand and went down to London on my own despite his advice.

But in those days you just didn't do those things. Not unless you had strong convictions and a solid belief in yourself, something which I most certainly did not have. "Lack of moral fibre" was the high-sounding name the army were now giving to that sort of behaviour, especially in the Great War. And as far as I was concerned they had now adapted it to suit in the bloody war we had just fought. And we all know now how that turned out. Who knows I may well have thrown away a successful career as a singer if I just had possessed the guts to oppose my father when I had the chance.

One thing however I had made my mind up about was to be nobody's fool. Smithy, Pricey and my old mates were now no more. I had to force myself to let them go and I think I did. They would understand I'm sure. They would be sympathetic towards me in my quest to build a life for myself, and my wife to be. May the boys rest in peace…

As my train approached Glasgow's Central Station I began to feel somewhat overcome. I was coming home. Home to the people and the city that I loved. I hated saying it but even Flensburg seemed a million miles away and momentarily my wife-to-be too. Was I doing the right thing? Should I go ahead with my request to have her brought to Scotland to marry me? I was beginning to feel slightly ashamed of my thoughts as the train slowed to a halt and I could see Charlie and Tam and my father waiting to greet me and to take me home.

It was then that I began to feel that churning feeling inside me again, something I hadn't felt for a long time. I was overjoyed to see them and they were glad to see me. We had all got out of that awful bloody war in our own individual way, Tam by sheer cunning and deviousness. Charlie too by his stint in the Middle East too came out unscathed and was about to marry soon. And myself. Had I really got out of it? Or was I still hearing those shells about to burst my ear drums? If I had any doubts, Tam soon dispelled them. "Good to see you, Ned."

He always called me Ned. I didn't know whether to approve or disapprove and I still don't to this day. Tam did things his way. Nobody told Tam what to do. He told them. "Hurry up, Ned and we'll get home and get something to eat. Then we'll go for a pot of beer." Tam seemed to be able to solve all his problems by going for a "pot" of beer. I often wished I could. I embraced my father. He was crying. So I didn't dwell too long on those thoughts of mine about Beardmore's and William Arrols and *Brylcream*. He hated me putting on *Brylcream*. I suppose he thought it wasn't manly. But I wasn't prepared to argue about such matters at that particular moment. It was just great to see them all again.

I got home to Warriston Street to my mother and sisters. That was to be another heart warming but tearful welcome. I had to wait somewhat till my mother took her arms from around me. It was as though she felt I was going to take off again almost immediately. But I was the youngest of seven. The last of the litter as was the saying then. And I suppose it was natural that my mother should be so upset. More so since she knew what my plans for the future were. I didn't want to hurt anyone. Nor was there any need to hurt anyone least alone my own family. I just hoped that Johanna as I was calling her now just to let it sound just that little less intimate would fit into the McCann family. That way I hoped no one would be hurt.

My mother had a lovely meal ready for me when I got home. There was Irish stew with those delicious little suet dumplings, which she always did so well. That was followed by semolina pudding with strawberry jam on top. To come up with even a sprinkling of strawberry jam in those days bordered on the ingenious because ration books were the order of the day. In fact I didn't think strawberry jam was even on the menu. But from wherever it came and it certainly wasn't from the McCann garden it was nevertheless welcome. And it tasted as succulent as always.

My three sisters, Kathleen, Rosina and Peggy, were of great assistance to my mother during those war years especially when the air raids came to Clydebank. And those salient points on the Clyde that the Germans had obviously ear-marked for special attention got that special attention and a lot of damage was done. Like everyone else of course we had the Anderson Shelter in the back garden and from what my sisters told me full use was made of that shelter when those sirens went off. My oldest sister then told me that when the occasion arose for them all to go to the shelter my mother would produce her rosary beads and prayers would be said aloud by her. And from what I heard she implored all the neighbours to join in. And most of them did. And most of them were Protestants. No one complained, in fact some of them probably enjoyed it. But then then that was my mother for you. The unpredictable Annie Mc. Cann . . .

It was difficult for me to talk about the war either to my own family or to the neighbours about my situation, even although my intentions were no longer a secret. In fact there were times when I just didn't know how to react. I only hoped that Hanni's permission to travel would be soon. Then and only then would a situation which at the moment I didn't know just how to handle would be solved once and for all. Of course I had to resist the usual implorings of my mother now and again. "Why can't you get a nice Catholic girl here, Eddie?" or "Why don't you take a trip over to Ireland? Sure you might find someone over there."

But despite the pleas, I just didn't want to see anyone else. To be perfectly honest, the only one who really stood solidly behind me was Tam. Charlie was just newly married and had moved away as had Johnnie my oldest brother. Tam and myself were the only men left at Carntyne with the exception of my father. And as a union delegate of Glasgow Corporation Water Department he didn't have any specific thoughts about it at all. To be perfectly frank my father didn't have any thoughts about anything bar union matters. Even my mother played second fiddle to Tom McCann's union affairs . . . In fact they say that my father had one claim to fame. And as far as I know it's recorded somewhere in the bowels of Glasgow Corporation's archives.

Being a worker with Glasgow Corporation Water Department meant, as many of us should know but probably didn't that many holes had to be dug up in the streets of Glasgow. And those aforesaid holes, it is laid down somewhere in some obscure rule book, had to be of a certain minimum circumference. This strict but very necessary edict was issued for reasons of health and safety and for the environment in general.

So cometh the day, cometh the man. And in the true tradition of that old adage along came Tom Mc.Cann. Who they say came up or should that be down, with the smallest ground hole ever dug in Glasgow Corporation's history. It was then called "McCann's Hole". Because he seemingly was the only one could get down it and the only one who could get back up out of it again. Just imagine the amount of overtime he must have raked in. I could only hope he told my mother all about it. And they do say that was one of the reasons he and Tam didn't hit it off. Whereas my father was a great union man, Tam wasn't. Not for any political reasons, I hasten to add. It was just that Tam wasn't in a job long enough to get round to joining any union.

Tam was with me all the way. Whether it was because I was the only one fit enough to see he didn't burn himself to death in bed some night I'll never know. But knowing Tam I doubted that. When he saw some of the photographs of Hanni he whistled with astonishment. "She's a smasher, Ned, and I mean that. I wish it was me." Now for our Tam to say something like that shook me. Because he said often and loud enough that he would never ever marry again after his late wife Isa died. "What are they all going to say when she arrives in this country?" I queried. "Don't worry about that. It'll be a nine day wonder and that'll be it. As far as I can see there's nothing to touch her here or anywhere else for that matter. So never mind what the old lady says, just you get out there and get a job and get things ready for her coming here. Now let's you and I go and get a pot of beer before they're shut."

I went with him willingly for that pint. And it was not only a pint that I got from Tam that night. He gave it to me straight knowing that I was ten years younger than he was. He also knew I was not nearly as experienced in world affairs as he was. He was also aware of my own nervous disposition, and put his arm around me. "Don't worry, Ned. That's your trouble. You worry too much. Get out there and get a job. Don't be afraid. We'll go and see the Celts on Saturday. No. On second thoughts we'd better not. That might make you worse. Ha ha. Come on drink up. Let's have another."

He held up his whisky glass. I've never known to this day, why Tam always said. "Let's go and have a pot of beer." For Tam drank very little beer. It was always whisky. Anyway, he raised his glass in a toast. "Here's to you and your fraulein, Ned. And the best of luck to you both." I felt great after that. And suddenly I didn't care whether I had to stand guard over him for a solid week or even a month. Tam had succeeded in firing me up. It was just what I needed. Now I knew I was ready to take them all on.

## Chapter Eight

*Frauleins Invade Harwich. . .*

It was a momentous day for me when I travelled to Harwich to meet my future wife and my child. My daughter would then be only a few weeks old. Emotions were running high. Tam came with me. He wanted to come and would have been my first choice had I to make one. He was all for it. So off we went and took sandwiches with us for the eight-hour plus train journey to Euston. Tam had also duly fortified himself with a few drams before leaving home. He also had a half bottle with him no doubt to be used only in emergencies. For once I didn't blame him. But I didn't join him in one either as I didn't feel like it somehow. I wanted to be in full control. Perhaps later I thought.

We crossed over from Euston to Liverpool Street station hence to Harwich. An hour and a half later we were there. Nor was I the only British soldier to be awaiting his sweetheart. From the Hook of Holland that boat now carrying her fair share of German frauleins was fast approaching a pier packed with British soldiers waiting impatiently for that long awaited embrace. It was the very first boat load of Germans, the female variety that is, to ever invade Britain to rousing cheers and whistles. They had succeeded where their male counterparts had failed miserably.

There was no doubting that there were some would not have had it. Would never have welcomed it. They were entitled to their point of view. No one disputes that. But were they there? Had they been over there? For therein lies the story. No matter the doubters. The welcome was there written indelibly on the faces of those British Army Of The Rhine soldiers who had dared to break with tradition and married the fair; In love and war. What was that old saying again? Many had sniggered and dubbed it "The Love Boat". Be that as it may.

As the boat docked all eyes were focused on the decks and those hats with the wide brims which set European women apart from their British counterparts. There were those who would say that a lot more than hats divided them. But I won't be dragged into that one. I was there to see my fraulein wide-brimmed hat or no.

Then I spotted her. She stood out from the rest. I nudged Tam's arm and pointed her out as she stood there on a deck that was packed with other frauleins, I watched his eyes as he stared at that vision aboard that boat. He stood aghast. "Well Tam?" I asked. "What do you think?" He opened his mouth to speak, then closed it again. I thought he looked slightly overcome. "What - what do I think?" I think she's the best looking bit of stuff on that boat, Ned. That's what I think.

And there's some smashers on that boat. But you've got the winner, Ned. There's no doubt about that. So on you go and greet them, and I'll go and get a trolley for all her stuff."

I was glad now that I had brought Tam along. He was a great help and seemed to revel in situations like this. He just oozed confidence. If only I'd been born with half of it I thought. Anyway I managed to push my way to the front where they would disembark. I almost got past the stevedore who stood at the end of the gangway in my haste to grab Hanni's arm; and would have fallen into the water had he not grabbed me. The stevedore smiled, steadied me then in a flash she was in my arms at last. I held her gently then looked down at the little buggy type pram she was pushing. She let me cradle our baby for a moment. And we stood in silence for a second then walked slowly to where Tam had managed to get a trolley for us. Yet again Tam was doing all the right things at the right time. And I was grateful.

I introduced Tam to Hanni and I held the baby momentarily. Tam closed his eyes. I could see he was near to tears. Perhaps he may have seen some similarity with his own late wife. He turned his head quickly and put Hanni's solitary case on the trolley. Hanni then tucked our daughter up well against the breeze from the sea and that was it. With Tam at the helm with the trolley our little convoy then began to weave our way through the milling crowds gathered there. Snatches of conversational German and English went the air. But it was that little bit more than just the mere phrase book English and German. "Meine Liebe, wie geht ist?" and the "Oh darling. How are you?" Which had taken over the conversational air space. And tearful embraces ensued. For history was unfolding on the dockside at Harwich that afternoon in late November in 1947.

We managed somehow to make it to the waiting train. Tam managed to get Hanni's case and the little collapsible buggy into the guard's van whilst I sought seating places on that packed to capacity train for London. Once more it was another scramble to get to Euston from Liverpool Street, but we managed it between us. I certainly couldn't have managed it on my own. Whatever else the outcome of my forthcoming marriage would be, it had certainly restored a lot of my respect for my big if somewhat at times wayward brother.

The journey from Euston to Glasgow was a nightmare. Seats were not only taken, they were over-taken. Everyone squeezed up together. The corridors were even worse. So bad were they that there wasn't one ticket collector to be seen never mind to plead to. A goodly sprinkling of the Allied forces were all there, soldiers, sailors, airmen, either going on leave or coming from leave; or just plain coming or going. They were all there.

Needless to say the usual gentlemanly overtures were made by the travelling servicemen. Hanni and another travelling lady were offered seats. And of course their offers were readily accepted. Hanni was offered a seat at the window as she was carrying a baby. It was all noble stuff. And it wasn't just because she was still wearing that large wide-brimmed hat either.

She warranted even more looks and open-mouthed stares when she took that hat off. And it was that gold blonde hair and those golden blue eyes that did it. She set that compartment alight at a stroke. One sailor after his eyes settled back in their sockets, came up with a brainwave. Why not let the baby sleep up on the luggage rack? It was certainly wide enough and deep enough and quite capable of holding a baby quite safely. It certainly made sense so after a quick removal of a suitcase I did just that with Hanni's help and our little daughter slept on as though she had been up in that luggage rack all her little life. Not only that but the sailor then offered to swap seats so that Hanni could sit opposite and thus keep a motherly eye on her baby. Not only that but it was a window seat which were always at a premium on trains.

Meanwhile I just sat there taking stock and keeping the proverbial eyes peeled; not forgetting for a moment that this train journey had a life span of from eight to ten hours. I was also aware that there was a lot of merriment and booze around also not necessarily in that order. Hanni and I didn't converse; and it was not just because we weren't sitting opposite each other.

Even I knew that the time was hardly ripe for a bit of conversational German. Not that I was afraid; but because I had already steeled myself as to what I would have to do from now on, even when we got off the train. Not that I was expecting anything nasty, but one just had to be prepared. So Hanni and I settled for just smiles and nods to each other from across a crowded compartment so to speak. I was determined to keep my nerve from now on. I was even beginning to amaze myself at the transitional stage that had come over me since being reunited with Hanni. It may well be that I felt that good old Smithy would always be with me in spirit. Or it could just be that I knew Tam was lying handy in the corridor and with just enough alcohol in him to be suitably equipped should anything go wrong.

After an extra long eleven and a half hours our train stuttered into Glasgow Central station. We scrambled ourselves into some sort of order, as best our weary bodies could. This was a time when being a baby was a very good person to be. For our daughter slept all the way through. Hanni with baby wrapped in a shawl in her arms and myself waited while Tam searched for a taxi.

Taxis weren't exactly thick on the ground then in 1947. Not being an over abundance of petrol around was the main reason for that. So our hopes weren't all that high as we stood there in the cold, waiting. A mere fifteen minutes later, Tam returned accompanied by a taxi and a driver. who just happened to know Tam when they'd both worked together as ratcatchers. Or to give that noble profession it's new post-war designation; "Rodent Exterminators." Not only would he take us all home to Carntyne, but he would do it for nothing after hearing about Tam's brother's special occasion.

About twenty minutes later Rab the taxi driver had us bowling along Alexandra Parade en route for Carntyne. The baby was still asleep, quite happy by all accounts. I wished I could say the same. Hanni was trying to peer out the window to see where we were going but it was dark. There was nothing to see. I sincerely hoped our future would be somewhat less bleak. Only now was I beginning to have slight misgivings about it all. What if Hanni couldn't settle down? Couldn't stand the hurly burly of life in Scotland. Maybe the whole thing would be too much for her.

The taxi stopped outside Warriston Street. The aforesaid convoy had arrived. As I said before taxis were a rarity in Carntyne as they were everywhere else in those bleak post-war days. They were even more rare when that taxi was occupied by an ex enemy; a German fraulein with her baby.

Now Carntyne for the uninformed got the name of being one of Glasgow's better class council housing estates situated on the fringes of Glasgow's East End. And where people always bought ice cream from a little Italian ice cream vendor with a barrow. It should also be noted that this little ice cream vendor conformed to the hygiene edict of the time. "And now wash your hands." And being within those strict confines of the law was perfectly acceptable to the good citizens of Carntyne. That cut above!

Some might even say it was almost on a par with Knightswood on the other side of the city which at that time got the name of being the council equivalent of Hollywood's Beverley Hills. And only sometimes bought ice cream. Whereas Carntyne's lone claim to territorial fame was that it was next to Riddrie, where people actually bought houses and not Ice Cream whether it was from a barrow or even later from a van. Then there was the famous or infamous Riddrie Knowes where people actually owned large houses and sometimes even mansions. But they were toffs and very rich, but never ever bought ice cream. And they lived more or less next door to the infamous Barlinnie Prison. However none of these things seemed to matter as I opened the gate for my fiancée and child.

Tam carried in the cases and the buggy. I was vaguely aware of the adroit pulling aside of curtains from across the road even at that early hour of the morning. Along the road from ours there was again just a hint of the movement of a curtain. Further along still on the other side someone had decided to pull up their blinds that bit early just to let that freezing but bracing November air rush into their living room. I was just grateful that it was too early for the ice cream men. It may well have lowered the tone.

My sisters opened the door. First it was Kathie the eldest. She somewhat shyly bowed her head and shook hands with Hanni then lifted the baby from her arms and kissed her. Rosina was next who did exactly the same; warmly but just slightly restrained. Then Peggy followed suit. It was all very civilised. My brother Charlie was next. He embraced Hanni gently then patted the baby. Next came my niece Frances, Tam's only daughter who would have been about twelve. She kissed Hanni enthusiastically then grabbed the baby in her arms and ran up the hall. My oldest brother Johnnie wasn't there because he was already married and lived a mile or so away in Shettleston. One less for the reception. And such things were important in those days

Then down the hall came my mother. She was crying and holding her rosary beads in her hands. This was going to be difficult I thought, but it wasn't. My mother, still in her dressing gown greeted us as I made the introduction. " Mammy. This is Hanni my fiancée; and my wife-to-be and our baby daughter." I didn't know quite what to expect. Whether it would be a quick command to all kneel on the floor for a decade of the rosary I knew not. Or whether it would be a mere sign of the cross and a sprinkling of the holy water or what. But none of these things happened.

She just stood back a little and gave Hanni an appraising look; tears streaming down her face then turned to me. "Does she not speak any English at all Eddie?" I nodded my head. "Yes. She speaks a little." Only then did my mother give Hanni a tearful embrace and I detected a "God bless". Whether Hanni qualified for the embrace and the "God bless." just because she could speak a little English or not I've never known to this day. But she got an embrace and a blessing from my mother. And as far as I was concerned that was one bridge crossed of which there could well be many more.

Our hall was in danger of being overcrowded so we moved on to the living room. And there he was my father still in his pyjamas and not in the least embarrassed. He greeted my future wife by excusing himself for not shaking hands with her. He then tried to explain with his own type of sign language that he had been lighting our coal fire. However he did stop long enough to give her a peck on the cheek. And believe me that was not a snub. That was my father being demonstrative. That living room coal fire was his pride and joy and woe betide anyone who tried to keep him from it. That fire, and the trade union drained any emotions he had. As a matter of fact I fully expected him at any moment to tell me to drop everything and get down to William Beardmore's again and those steelwork gates right away.

We finally settled down to breakfast. And my mother had done us proud. Porridge, toast, and plates of scrambled eggs, were placed in front of each one of us . Before sitting down herself she asked my niece Frances to hand her the baby. Then as though seeking Hanni's permission with an incline of her head she placed our daughter gently on the bed. She then sat down herself at the table. I got the impression that my mother was indicating to us all, that coping with one baby shouldn't be a problem. Having a baby out of wedlock was another matter however and no doubt that would be dealt with by her, in due course. Hanni could have been a latter day Mata Hari. That wasn't all that important. Being German either didn't present any major problems. The over-riding factor was that she wasn't a Catholic. That was the cardinal sin.

Breakfast was a strained affair and I wished desperately that it was over. We were all tired. Hanni more than any I felt. So I had a quiet word with Rosina one of the more worldly of my sisters and she took her down to rest in her bed. My other two sisters looked after the baby. After the breakfast things were cleared away Frances played a few tunes on our old piano no doubt to try and cheer the place up a bit. But it didn't work somehow. I tried to steer clear of my mother for as long as I possibly could. My try wasn't quite good enough however for she collared me in the hall just as I was about to stand outside the door to collect my thoughts.

" Now then Eddie; you'll have to go to the chapel and see the parish priest because you'll have to get married as quickly as possible." Even I knew that so I promised to go round as soon as I could. There was no one who wanted the wedding over quicker then I did. Although I didn't know how Hanni would feel about it all. As yet she had never been consulted. All the urgency was coming from the McCanns. "She'll have to take instruction, you know; if she wants to be a Catholic that is." I knew that too. But it wasn't something that was high on my list of priorities at that particular moment. But I thought I'd better put my mother's fears to rest and decided to go round that afternoon to see the priest.

St. Thomas's in Riddrie was a nice little chapel and after a confab with the priest who I may say was very helpful, he agreed to marry us the following week.

But he would require to see and talk with Hanni to straighten out a few details. The priest also explained to me that she couldn't be married at the altar since she was a non Catholic. This I knew; however I explained as best I could to Hanni. She was a little surprised. Even disappointed, I fear, but finally accepted the church's ruling.

And so we were married in St Thomas's in 1947; married in the vestry, that is. A kind of back-door wedding with Hanni promising that she would not stand in the way of the children being brought up to be Catholics. But to me, it was a marriage nonetheless and I breathed freely for a while at least. We had a small reception in the church hall afterwards with a somewhat restricted meal on the menu since those were austere times. But with a lot of good will and just a little assistance from the black market we managed to put up a reasonably good meal with the booze lovingly contributed by Tam and some of his drinking pals. And a great day and night, it should be stressed, was eventually held by one and all.

Housing of course would be the next problem we would have to face. I was fully aware of that old folk's tale about two women in the one kitchen and made up my mind to act with alacrity. Because not only was I faced with two women with different ideas in the one house, I had two women with differing thoughts talking different languages together. That in itself could cause a lot of trouble. So swift action was called for. And there was also that little matter of getting a job too.

But getting a house became my number one priority. Glasgow Corporation Housing Department were not at all sympathetic however. Did I not know that I wasn't the only one who'd been away to war, was just married, and had a child? What about the poor Glasgow Corporation clerks who couldn't get away to war? And what about those poor unfortunates who just happened to be in reserved occupations when the war started? Were they given a house to live in? Bet your bloody life they were, I thought. So no joy there.

Tam was now driving long distance haulage trucks for a living. He'd packed in his last job, which just happened to be with a firm who had just began to produce a brand new product for the consumer market. They were called potato crisps. He quite liked the job at first, but confessed he liked the crisps even more. And believe you me he kept the whole of the McCann family going by carting home loads of those crisps in a large cardboard box. We began to get them for breakfast, dinner and tea. Those crisps were a revolution of their day.

The snag was he told me later, that the firm hadn't quite been able to come up with a method of how to package the crisps. This meant that potential customers had to bring their own containers or paper bags to get them filled. And therein lies the tale of Tam's not entirely amicable parting from that firm with the revolutionary new product and it's packaging problems. It took them an awful long time to come up with the packaging side of things. But Tam sorted the problem out a lot quicker. The story goes that he was extra generous one night with his take-home portion of crisps. He chose a cardboard box that unfortunately had holes in it and this unfortunately left a tell tale trail of crisps from the factory that led to Tam's bus stop, on to the bus and then on to our very own gate. Not only had that firm a packaging problem they were now facing a huge deficit in profits. So exit Tam from another job "with prospects" . . .

Despite his upsets the enterprising Tam was getting jobs whereas I wasn't. I was even tempted to go back to a certain bakery I'd worked at just after my demob, but resisted that temptation almost immediately. And I was seeing less and less of my wife and my daughter because of my quest for jobs and at the same time searching for a place of our own. Hanni I knew must be getting bored. And the last thing I wanted was for her to become homesick.

All of the newspapers were carrying stories of homesick frauleins, and how the they were finding it difficult to settle down to their new way of life in Britain. I tried to do my part as best I could given the circumstances. But I was getting the feeling that it wouldn't be enough if I didn't do something positive very soon. Hanni was a very positive type of person. A very thin but very sinewy independent streak ran through her. For I knew her only too well.

It wasn't that my mother wasn't doing the right thing by her. No. It was just that the void between them was too great. I took Hanni to Mass every Sunday just to please my mother. But it was merely academic as far as she was concerned I'm sure. The Mass was said in Latin. She was German. Many of the litanys were in English. So where did that put her? Or even worse where did that leave me. But to be fair she took it all in her stride without complaint. But for how long? I wondered.

In between looking for a job and a house, Hanni and I and our baby Joan in her little continental buggy would go for long walks up Ruchazie Road towards a huge water tower where just below it, nestled an old people's home. No longer there alas. It was a beautiful spot. Sometimes we would bring sandwiches and make an afternoon of it just sitting there in the grass kissing and cuddling for as long as we dared. We would then trundle slowly back down the slight hill towards home. And we were still getting long lingering glances from people we passed. And it wasn't just that unusual type of continental little pram that their gazes were fastening on either. Nor was it me.

Hanni was still managing to keep her feelings in check despite still living with her in-laws. But only just I suspect. For she could be as rebellious as any when the notion took her as I knew from those Naafi days in Flensburg. A friend told me that there was now a club in Glasgow where frauleins could meet. It had been formed by a fraulein in similar circumstances seemingly to combat the chances of them getting homesick and to give them a chance to chat to each other in their own tongue.

But Hanni didn't want to know about the club. All she wanted she told me in no uncertain terms was a house of her own and to be able to make her own decisions. She was a woman who knew what she wanted. Even though she had been here only a matter of months she already had a good working knowledge of the ration book. She wasn't long in getting to know how many coupons bought what. And at my mother's instructions had done a fair bit of shopping unaided. The pressures were back on me once more. And this was something I could have well done without.

But it was to be another few weeks before I heard the good news. And again it was that man Tam who was responsible for the break-through. A friend of a friend of his had heard that an elderly widower who also lived in Carntyne was looking for lodgers as his daughter and her family who had lived with him for some time were now moving to England. Hanni and myself were soon at his door for an interview.

The house had three bedrooms similar to our own in Warriston Street with a small manageable back and front garden. Ideal I thought, as did Hanni. She had mistakenly thought that the old man himself would be moving out. I then explained the situation to her, stressing that the time couldn't be all that far off when we could get our own council house. She was reasonably happy with the little garden and the exterior in general, but she still wasn't happy about the state of the interior of the house. And much as she was desperate to get away from her in-laws, the house she said was not for her. I tried for the next hour to talk her round but she was and always had been a stickler for hygiene. She didn't want it. So I eventually gave up. Thus we were still homeless. I was certainly not having my troubles to seek.

I had hoped against hope that she would take the house. Even if it was only for a few weeks. Because I knew she could have transformed that place in no time. She would have gutted it out and it would also have given her something to do. It would also have kept her mind off other things. Like her folks back home in Flensburg. And I knew deep down that she was getting more than just a little homesick.

Things weren't quite going my way. And if I didn't get cracking there was always the chance that she would just give me an ultimatum one day, and say. " Either get me a proper house or I'm going back home to Flensburg." To say that things weren't going my way would be to put it mildly. Then at last I got a break. At least I hoped I had.

Right out of the blue I was offered a fortnight's work as a barman and I jumped at the chance. It would do till something else came along. It would be a hard slog. And all for £3 a week. The pub was situated just before Charing Cross. The charge-hand (well named) could well have qualified as the swindler of the century. Ironically at that time it was reputed to be the only pub in Glasgow where singing was allowed. Whether it was just because it was frequented mainly by students or not I didn't know. But one thing was for sure. Licensed to sing or not. Little did they know, they had nothing to sing about.

For the man in charge, Donald a big Highlander was one of the biggest crooks I reckon I'd ever came across in a long time. And I'd met a few in my time. Both in the army and out of the army. On my very first day and just before the pub doors opened he stood with me in front of the gantry where all the spirits were lined up. He then pulled me aside and slyly informed me that the "In Drink" for the female students who frequented his pub was a "Pimms Number One."

He then elaborated still further by listing them to me with his fingers. "There's a Pimms Number One. A Pimms Number Two. And a Pimms Number three." Maybe he thought I couldn't count, hence the fingers. The demonstration then followed. "First of all you take a big cocktail glass stuff it with the two slices of orange, three slices of lemon, plenty of ice and a glacé cherry with a stick through it." He gave me another sly glance here. "I hope you're taking all this in?"

I glared back at him; dwelt as long as I dared on the dire state of my finances bit my lip and nodded. "Right. When you've got your orange, lemon, and cherry in you then just add your Pimms." He demonstrated this by adding one flick of the bottle's contents into the fruity concoction that was already filling the glass. The measure of Pimms that was flicked into that drink was minuscule. About a thimble full of spirit I reckoned went in and no more. He then went on. "You then give the whole thing a good stir with the swizzlestick and Presto!" That's your Pimms Number One. . .

I couldn't believe my eyes at first. It was daylight robbery committed at night. especially perpetrated at week-ends on unsuspecting students who could ill afford it I thought. And to think good friends of mine had been blown up to safeguard crooks like that. It angered me more than a little and I was tempted once more to tell him that . . . I looked at him hard and fast after the demonstration, then I tried a little sarcasm on him. "And what about a Pimms Number Two?" And yes, you're right. He returned my probe just as glibly. "You just cut back on the lemon . . . !"

The pub was virtually empty during the day. But in the evenings and at weekends particularly it was jam-packed with young students of both sexes drinking and singing away merrily. Well, singing anyway. He didn't trust me all that much, did our charge-hand. Maybe he thought I had too honest a face. Mind you I was tempted to shop him in front of them all on one Saturday night in particular.

It had gone closing time and I was standing at the door calling "Time please". which was part of my duties. Then out came a young couple arm in arm; and she was whispering coyly into her boyfriend's ear. "Would you believe it. I've had six of those Pimms, darling and I'm not the least bit tiddly." I was sorely tempted to say to her as she passed, "Listen, my dear. You could have had twenty six and you still wouldn't even have been the slightest bit "tiddly". But I could see him watching me out of the corner of my eye so I resisted the temptation. But I was still determined to get him. And I swore to myself that I would, if only for the hell of it . . . And to get a bit of my own back . . .

I did manage it. I got my own back. It was on my very last day. Revenge they say is sweet. But this one couldn't have been sweeter. It was in the afternoon just before we closed at 2.30 p.m. prompt. The pub was almost empty and our master thief was standing talking to a customer and trying to keep his eye on me behind the bar at the same time . . .

Like they do in the best magic circle shows, what he didn't know was that earlier I had secreted almost a half glass of neat Gordon's gin down on the draining board below the bar and away to the back where it would not be seen. I had it standing alongside other similar glasses. It wasn't a new scam, but I just thought I'd give it a try for old times' sake. Another old army game. . .

The first thing was to draw attention to yourself. This you did, for that way no one would dream that you were going to pull a fast one. So you first of all let the water run fast and loud from the tap below the bar. And then you held up high a half pint glass full of that water as though you were ensuring that it was nice and clear whilst the water gushed away. You then took a sip and put the glass down below the bar as though having a rest between sips.

It was then you picked up the half pint glass of gin that was positioned there, held it aloft and shouted out loudly. "Cheers everyone!" And as expected a couple of punters would reply back with their glasses raised, and toast you as if on cue.

"Cheers." I even got a half smile from that crooked charge-hand as he watched. It may have savoured of dishonesty on my part. But I just thought I would strike a blow for those poor students... And the ironic bit about it was, I hated gin!

When I got home Hanni smelt drink off me and thought for a moment I had been out with Tam. And it took quite a time for me to convince her that I hadn't. But despite my protestations, it was the watery mince treatment for the next day or so... But she still wanted that home of her own. So I had to listen to it all over again. I went up again next day to the Housing Department and pressed them once more about getting a council house.

But I got the same answers as before. I would have to wait my turn. Everyone was in the same boat. Knowing my luck, that boat could well be the *Titanic.* In fact that was how it was to be. My second child was born and we still didn't have a house yet. So much for a home fit for bloody heroes I thought. I wasn't looking for any special treatment but I did hear that even in England soldiers were being given more sympathetic hearings than we were.

Maybe I would be better giving this mental hospital thing a try. I'd been told that if you had a head condition such as mine that it could help to get you a pension. I didn't want to go. Maybe they would keep me in. I was getting desperate. I had to give it a bit of thought. Go to the British Legion someone told me... But what if people talked. Let them talk. A pension was a pension. Money was money. And I had neither. And I had to live. I went back to the counter in that housing place and apologised for losing my patience. I also told them that I couldn't help it. That it was just the way my head was.

And they accepted my apology. Not only that they sympathised with me. Then another clerk came over with my housing application. "Look," he said. "I see here that your second child is a boy. And you already have a girl. So that should help your case a lot." I apologised to them all again. They said they would look at my case again with regards to my claim for a house. And this heartened me somewhat.

Then a stroke of luck; I spotted the advert in the *Daily Record* "Singers wanted for forthcoming 1949-50 Cinderella pantomime in Glasgow Alhambra. Auditions to be held from 9a.m. on Monday." The Alhambra often had the longest running pantomime in the whole of Great Britain usually running for twelve weeks. So it would be quite a coup if I were to be picked. So I did a bit of quiet rehearsing of the popular songs of the day. I rehearsed in the bathroom, in the street, even walking down for the auditions. And what a shock I got when I turned the corner into Sauchiehall Street.

There were even more people waiting for those auditions than the previous ones I had attended for Jack Hylton before the war. The queues stretched right down West Nile Street and went on more or less for ever. I tried to count the numbers but gave up and began rehearsing to myself, regardless. Hanni had given me her blessing. And there was generosity for you. Because she now had another baby to look after. My son Charles was born as well as everything else. And that kept her busy. Baby-sitting was not an option in those days.

I thought to myself that if I did ever make it to the top or anywhere near the top it would be her I would have to thank. But my sisters did agree to help out. And I also promised to get her home to Flensburg for a holiday. So I thought to myself; Mc.Cann you'd better get cracking. And got cracking I did. I stood in that queue for about five hours. Nor was it the quickest moving of queues. As queues go it moved forward an inch every ten minutes or so. Frustration was beginning to set in. More so when it began to rain. Still hardly a soul moved out of that queue. Fame wasn't necessarily the spur here. But money was.

Eventually my turn in the queue reached the stage door through which we would enter with our sheet music as laid down. I didn't have any sheet music for what I was going to sing. I just wanted to sing and hoped they would accept that. Because I'd always been used to those church concerts where sometimes there would be no pianist at all. And if it did run to a pianist all you got was a perfunctory, "Just you start and I'll follow you" sort of thing. So it didn't worry me unduly.

There was only one turn in front of me, a young girl. As we were now inside the auditorium we both watched the opposition. One was on stage at that moment. He was a tallish young man who handed down his music sheet to the pianist just below the stage. The theatre was in total darkness apart from the seats which were covered with white sheets. It was like being in a cemetery, with a grave keeper who had a passion for white headstones. And it felt just as eerie. In the centre sat one man, and he was the voice of authority.

The pianist struck up the intro and the young hopeful on stage sprang suddenly into action. Striding out sailor-fashion up and down the stage as he belted out. "The Fleet's In Port Again. Back Home In Port Again. Yo Ho.Yo Ho. And We'll Have a Jolly Good Time. The Fleet's In Port Again. . . " Then the voice of the invisible man in the centre of the auditorium boomed out "Thank you. That will do!"

But our agile performer out there on stage was still doing his sailors hornpipe routine and peering out into an imaginary ocean à la Fred Astaire, but a non-dancing and slightly off-key Fred Astaire it had to be said as he sang and strutted up and down the stage. Nor had he heard or didn't want to hear the voice of authority. So he carried on regardless into the second verse. "Back Home In Port Again. Yo Ho Yo Yo. . . And We'll have A Jolly Good..Really. Marvellous. . . "

"Thank you. That will do. Please leave the stage.! "The performing "sailor" then stopped dead in his tracks and peered into the darkness of the auditorium to see where the invisible voice was coming from. "Thank you. Please leave the stage." The impersonal nasal voice barked out again from the bowels of the theatre. "But I- I haven't finished yet. The best bit's still to come . . . " insisted our performing hornpiper. He then got down on his knees so that he could see better whoever it was or whatever it was that was destroying his routine. Undeterred and on hearing no further destructive interruptions from the darkness of the auditorium our "Fred Astaire" promptly got to his feet and into his musical act again as though he had never been away. . . "The Fleet's In Port Again. Back Home In . . . "

"Thank you. Thank you. Thank you. Now please leave the stage or I shall have you ejected!" The message this time was unambiguous. "Fred" stopped dead in his tracks and cupped a hand to his eyes to still try and see where the message was coming from then stomped off stage. As he passed he whispered to me out of the side of his mouth. "What fucking chance have you got, Jimmy, eh? Bastards!"

I was inclined to agree with him but kept my mouth shut. I was watching the girl who was before me up on that stage. I was next. The old heart was thumping. Hardly the best of hobbies for a bomb-happy bugger like myself I thought. But I was determined to see it through and get a few quid by me for the wife and kids even if it proved disastrous in the long run. "Next." That was me I told myself and walked on stage striving to bring moisture to bone dry lips. I bent down to where the pianist was in the orchestra pit and apologised for not having any sheet music. I figured honesty was the best approach. At least then my tombstone could read. "He was duff. But he was honest!"

The pianist was surprisingly accommodating. "OK then. So what are you going to sing for us?" Perhaps he was thinking; anything's got to better than that Scottish Fred Astaire. . . "I would like to sing" The Isle Of Innisfree ," I said as modestly as I could. It was one I'd heard Bing at and I thought I could handle it. "Let's hear it then," he said.

My heart was thumping like mad when I heard the pianist's perfect intro and surprising even myself began singing in my best baritone voice. As I sang I was conscious as any aspiring singer would of those five words that can halt you right bang in the the middle of your song. But fortunately for me those dreaded words, "Thank you. That will do." didn't come.

Instead I got a terse "Thank you. Kindly leave your name with the pianist." Inwardly I knew I'd got away with it. Still you're always sorry for the other fellow. But I had been the other fellow for too long and I thought I had a right to my turn. And I had a wife and two children to feed. And most certainly the army nor the War Office weren't going to do it for me. So I had no cause to feel guilty about winning through for a little while. A moment of glory. I hoped the children would be proud of their daddy.

Six singers only were picked from those mile long queues so I took a certain amount of satisfaction from that. I couldn't be all that bad I thought. Our job was to be a kind of backing group to the principal boy in the pantomime. We were supposed to represent a new and more manly type of post-war chorus boy as against the old cissy type of camp followers who were around at that time. We decided amongst ourselved that we weren't all that happy with the "chorus boy" designation thing anyway. But it was money . . .

But we gasped then relented when they told us we would be paid seven quid a week. And that was a lot of money then. Much higher than the average wage, which was around three or four pounds a week. And the job would last for twelve weeks. The only snag was that we would be required to do a matinée from 2 till 5 p.m. every Wednesday and Saturday. My wife was overjoyed when I told her I had been picked. And I think then, she had her own ideas as how to spend all that money every week for twelve weeks.

The Pantomime opened a week before Christmas to packed houses every night. But it was hard graft and we had a lot of singing to do. The principals were Harry Gordon and Alex Findlay and Bert and Doris Hare; big names around that time. Where they had their own individual dressing rooms we had unfortunately to rush into the lift to six floors up to share our dressing rooms.

We also had a dozen chorus girls. But unfortunately they were in different dressing rooms although still up in the gods like us. It was a novel experience for all of us. Because we all thought that we could fit this experience in with our day jobs. But that was soon knocked on the head when we were forced to join the actors union, Equity. Even although it was only for twelve weeks work.

The whole of Carntyne had heard about my good fortune. "Eddie McCann's in the Alhambra as a singing chorus boy. Did you hear about it? Just think of the money he'll be making!" It wouldn't be difficult to guess the topic of conversation. in and around the shops in Gartcraig Road. Especially, in the Co-op. One good thing about being a performer in those days was that you got a lot of perks. And one of those perks was getting into other shows free.

Wives and children belonging to any Equity members could get into any show or pantomime in the city of Glasgow for nothing. And they could go as often as they liked. Often on a Wednesday I would pull back the fire curtains to look out at the audience. And there in the best seats would be Hanni, Joan and her little brother Charles. It pleased me enormously. It was even more pleasing when the pantomime story was unfolding and we would be fencing around the principal boy on stage with our silly wooden swords. Then I could see Hanni pointing out their silly little daddy to them. . .

But it was a very long day. Much longer and much more tiring than we had anticipated; especially on matinee days. We spent an inordinate amount of time waiting and listening for our cues. Then it was a scamper to get down the lift and on to the stage on time. It was all very time consuming and all very boring. Even with those chorus girls around.

It was then that I came up with what I thought was a brilliant idea. We had all been picked because of our singing qualities. So why not put those voices to good use. We were all working class blokes. One was a bricklayer, one a piano tuner, and another was a joiner. And the rest of us had been unemployed up to now, "Why not form a quartet?" I said one afternoon when we were all sprawling about in the dressing rooms away up in the gods awaiting our music cue . . .

"A good idea," said one guy from Kilbirnie who was a first class tenor. And I mean first class. He sang "My Love Is like a Red Red Rose," for us one afternoon. It was superb. He agreed to be one of the quartet. But warned us that he was awaiting an audition for the D'oyly Carte Opera Company and if it came he was off. For seemingly it was an honour just to be heard by them. Naturally we agreed. And went straight into our own rehearsals up there in that dressing room.

"Close harmony" was the going thing then unlike today, when all group sang off the same pitch. That meant that "Third Part Harmony," had to be learned. And as I wasn't too good at that I was given the job of singing the melody straight. Or should I say as straight as I could. The present day title would be the grand one of "lead singer." The next thing to do was to learn the songs of the day, which then were "How Can You Buy Killarney," "Dem Bones Dem Bones Dem Dry Bones" and "Little Jimmy Brown."

We rehearsed every afternoon and night to plenty of applause from the girls in our dressing rooms till we thought we were more or less perfect. Our piano tuner did the scoring of the harmonies so we were fortunate there. Because not everyone could read music. But once he thought we had things just right we raced round the corner from the theatre to Biggars. They were the music people on the corner and there we made a record. It was a pot-pourri of the three afore mentioned songs plus another kind of theme song running through. We had to pay for it of course. But it was quite effective even if I say so myself. Were we ahead of our time I often ask myself?

The reason I thought of forming the quartet was not just because we had time on our hands. It was because there were was a distinct dearth of those kind of singing groups round about that time. That is If you excluded The Mills Brothers and The Andrews Sisters. But we were none of these famous people Nor did we ever try to be. We just did it. It gave us something to do. And we enjoyed doing it. I even came up with a name for us. And the name? None other than The Mellowtones. Hardly a household name you may say. But it could have been. Anyway, we had great fun doing it.

We then decided to do what we were told the professionals do, and that meant, "dressing" the act. And it meant just that. So the four of us went down to Frasers, in Argyle Street, and bought four two piece grey checked suits of the very same colour. After that, we bought two black bow ties. And so The Mellowtones were dressed very well, if not very famous.

The theatre manager was so impressed when he heard our record that he said he would play it over the tannoy some night when the show was over so that Messrs Gordon and Findlay and company could hear us and possibly book us. But that didn't happen. I suppose it was all a matter of taste which, there was no accounting for. As one of our group sarcastically said afterwards. "Some people still think Harry Gordon's a comedian." But we shall say no more on that score.

But we did get a few gigs the few weeks while we were operating. We did a charity show for the Jewish Board of Guardians in the Empire. We also played on the same bill as "Charlie Chester and his Gang," when they were playing Glasgow's Pavilion. We didn't make an awful lot of money mind you but we got lots to eat and drink afterwards and that was a novelty to we newcomers to the business. So we always delved in to the grub and the booze to compensate for the absence of any fees.

When the Alhambra's mammoth twelve week pantomime stint was over we were all very sad indeed. Not only that, but we had matured as a group and were desperate for work. A theatrical agent came up the last week of the panto to hear us. The word had got out. So he listened to us in the Green Room as we performed for him. And for about fifteen minutes he was all ears and appreciative. "How would you boys, or should I call you,The Mellowtones, like to play a summer season down at Rothesay Pavilion, this summer?" he said chomping on his cigar. "And what sort of wages would we be getting?" I asked him being the agreed spokesman. "How about twenty quid for a week." he said chortling as he spoke.

"Smashing," I shouted gleefully with the rest. "You're on. We'll take it." I then turned to the rest of the group. "Just imagine, lads. Twenty quid each for the whole of the summer season. Hooray." Then the agent interjected swiftly. "Wo. Wo. Wait a minute. When I said twenty quid. I didn't mean twenty quid each a week. I meant twenty quid for the act. For twenty quid I can get two first class bloody comics."

Crestfallen wasn't the word for it. We were well and truly shattered. Our dreams of stardom it would appear were at an end. But were we downhearted? You can bet your boots we were. So don't believe those actor types when they tell you that it's hard graft being an actor or an entertainer. It may well be. But it's still better than working. But at a fiver a week we just couldn't afford to stick it out. And bear in mind I had a wife and two kids to feed by this time. We discussed it amongst ourselves. Good as our act was we weren't committed enough to carry on. And there and then we decided unanimously to dissolve The Mellowtones. It had indeed been a great experience for us amateurs. We had savoured success. Fame indeed was the spur. Even if it was only for twelve weeks . . .

## Chapter Nine

*Earning a Crust in Glasgow*

Coming back down to earth again with the proverbial bang wasn't easy for a mere mortal like myself to take. But a few weeks after the pantomime season ended the bitter pill of despair was sweetened by a letter from the housing department, and it was great news. We had been allocated a three apartment house in a new council estate. Deep down, I knew that my wife would have preferred a house with a nice little garden but that wasn't to be. What we got was a top flat with a veranda, which to some extent helped ease the pain of not having a garden. It was also on the sunny side of the street, which had to be a plus.

We were installed within a week and the neighbours were very friendly indeed. Even when they discovered my wife was from Germany. It didn't seem to make any difference and to me that said a lot for the Scottish people because bear in mind this was the mid-nineteen fifties and the war was still very much on a lot of peoples minds. Hanni threw herself into the decorating of the rooms mostly on her own because painting and wallpapering were never nor ever have been my particular forte.

We now had a house of our owntwo nice healthy children and the proverbial world at our feet. Another plus was that our house wasn't exactly a million miles away from Celtic Park either, and I hadn't seen The Bh'oys in months. Sources close to me however had informed me that this wasn't necessarily a good thing. For it was rumoured then that to be entertained, was not to be at Celtic Park. I refused to believe that and felt I should go and judge for myself. But before I could do that I would have to find me a job.

So it was once more another case of another Labour Exchange in another part of the city. And although the location may have moved the Situations Vacant columns inside those newspapers hadn't. Plenty of vacancies as usual for hotel workers with the usual starvation wages. Par for the course I thought and it made me mad. Imagine anyone working for that kind of money. "Are you Five foot ten or over?" one poster shrieked, looking for answers. "Then Look No Further. Join The Police Force. Be A Citizen's Citizen And Become A Policeman. Good Pay. And Good Prospects. Excellent Career Move."

There would be plenty of punters for that I don't think. Within the circles I moved it took me a while to think of one who had made it to five feet six never mind anything else. Didn't they know this was Glasgow where the average height of a man was five feet five inches. Just an inch or so higher than myself at full stretch. There was certainly no sign of any queues for that one. I moved further along doing my best to try and take in all the tantalizing and mouth- watering stuff on offer. "Join The Army And See The World." was another poster adorning a wall. They weren't exactly knocking each other over to get to that one either. "Aye and see the next bloody world," hissed another dejected job seeker into my ear who looked as though he felt just as lucky as I was to get out of the last one alive and kicking . . .

"Wanted. Despatch Clerk for well known firm of bakers in Glasgow's East End." I managed to step up a gear and passed swiftly on after reading that one. I wondered to myself if wee Albert was still there plucking out those loaves as meticulously as ever. "Why Not Make The Railway Your Career?" I read on further. "British Railways Are Seeking Men Of Good character and Sound Education For Positions as Clerks. Successful Applicants Will Receive Commensurate Salary to Designation. Free Travel also provided." I never ever quite understood what that word commensurate meant. But I figured that it meant a fair day's pay for a fair day's work. And being a reasonable sort of man I was prepared to settle for that.

The reference thing could be a bit of problem but I was determined to give it a whirl. So I made my way up to Buchanan Street Station for an interview. As far as I was concerned the free travel thing was of potentially more value to me than the commensurate stuff, because it may well be a means of getting my wife home for her first holiday. It would appear that everyone wanted to be a Railwayman, myself included. But then wasn't it every child's dream to grow up and be a train driver? Buchanan Street passenger station was a very busy terminal serving most places north of Glasgow like Stirling, Perth and Aberdeen. They were apparently looking for a few booking clerks during the summer months with a view to becoming permanent if found to be suitable. That'll do for me I thought and began to read up a bit about Aberdeen and Perth and all points north just in case.

The interviewer was a tall thin man in his sixties. And he studied me the moment I entered a room within the main booking office. He shook hands with me. It was a straightforward handshake and not the funny kind, for which I was grateful. Whatever else he was he wasn't an apron-puncher I remember thinking. "Ah, so you're Mr.Mc.Cann. I'm Mr. Webster the Chief Booking Clerk." He didn't speak but rather fired words from his mouth like a machine gun fired bullets. "We're after young men who can handle the public. Most important. Smart, articulate. Know what they're doing. Good timekeepers. Play the game with us. We'll play the game with you. Good at figures?" He was talking in shorthand. I began to wonder how many words a minute he could do. I'd scarcely time to take a breath to answer. "Are you?"

"Am I what, Mr Mr?" I was floundering. I'd committed the cardinal error. I'd forgotten "Mr Pitman's" name. "Forgotten my name eh? Don't worry about it. It's Webster. Just think. American Dictionary. That'll keep you in mind. Good at figures? Dear, Dear. Asked you that, haven't I?" I gulped. "Y-Yes. I - I've never had much of a problem with figures Mr eh Mr er - Webster." He stroked his chin and looked straight at me . . .

"Four first class tickets to Aberdeen at seventeen and six?" he fired. "What?" I stammered, puzzled. "How much?" He was testing me. I racked my brains and began counting in my head. "Seventy shillings," I shouted. "Three Pounds ten shillings sir." He beamed over at me. "Good. Excellent. Do for me." He looked down at his notes for a moment. "Ex-Serviceman. Splendid. First war myself. Got to do your bit. Will let you know Mr McCann. First impressions. Good chance." Before I could draw another breath he had me outside that door wondering what had hit me. No doubt about it, Mr Webster's movements more than matched the rapidity of his verbiage.

As I made my way home I thought to myself that I had the makings of a good railway clerk. This was borne out by the fact that I had actually to restrain myself from giving a touch to that typewriter I'd seen when I was in that Booking office. I felt good and was quietly confident about my chances. For once I'd been lucky. He'd never even asked for references. Perhaps he'd forgotten. Then again, perhaps not. I may yet have to bring into play my prowess as a "forger." But I decided to worry about that bridge when the crossing confronted me.

I kept telling myself that it was a great time to be alive. I was feeling better. And I was able to hold my nerves in check with the aid of a little self discipline. They could keep their institutions and pensions. I could learn to manage without them thank you very much. We were well into the second half of the twentieth century, and less than fifty from the Big One. The Extremely Big Two Thousand.

I decided there and then to celebrate my good job interview with a visit to Parkhead the following Saturday to see Celtic. That's if I could manage the money and Hanni's blessing. Not necessarily in that order, I hasten to add. But first things first. All those interviews for jobs and one thing and another were beginning to have a telling effect on my wardrobe. But suits cost money.

It was then I spotted the advert in *The Glasgow Evening Times*. "Credit With Dignity." And somehow it clicked with me being of a sartorial bent. It had a ring to it. And could well be the textile revolution of the century. It was just what I'd been looking for. The advert went on to say that for a ridiculously small down payment I could be the possessor of three suits at one time. And there was a further bonus. If you recommended and were successful in recommending C.W.D. to your friends you could earn enough commission to get yourself another drape.

Now I would be the first to admit that this new far-seeing revolutionary firm could mean the demise of "The Fifty Bob Tailors"and that good old standby "The West End Misfits". And that would sadden me. Because I had a certain affinity with both of them in the past. But progress was progress. And it would be a brave man who would stand in the way of that progress. Very soon I became their flagship and must have been high on C.W.Ds list of prized customers having recommended them to more than a few of my acquaintances. Nor had I any hesitation in so doing.

Because not to put too fine a point on it, C.W.D. were making it possible for me and people like me to have a brand new suit on without the wearer having as much as a penny in his pocket. One such customer I had won over from the credit people was a little bloke named Vince McGlubligan. Some may cynically say that he was ripe for winning over. OK so wee Vince wasn't quite Brain of Britain material and thought that "carnal knowledge." was someone who was well up in confectionery. But like myself he had a leaning towards the sartorial side of life. And again like me was very happy with his suits.

Before meeting me Vince had hitherto thought that all men's suits were made to measure for someone else and never for him. He, like me, not being a "stock size" as they say in the trade.. Vince used to think that all tailors used to hammer wooden dummies together and stitch trousers and jackets on to them. Then sit back and wait for someone to come along suitably deformed so that the garment would fit But nothing could be further from the truth I told him before introducing him to C.W.D.

It was pleasing indeed to know that the days of a tailor ramming an arm up the back of your jacket and telling you it fitted you to perfection were over. And there was no one more pleased to hear that than wee "Totties and Mince". It was as though a whole new textile world was unfurling in front of his very eyes.

But just in case anyone thought for one moment that C.W.D. were some great philanthropic institution dreamed up by some charitable outfit or other they would require to think again. Those precious suits weren't handed out willy-nilly. Every prospective client's background was rigorously but discreetly checked. Your name and your address were noted. And your previous address too; and the one before that and then your next of kin. But it was all handled with great sensitivity.

They were strict. Even I would go along with that. Vince thought they were too strict. And hinted as much to me that before he could secure his latest little Donegal tweed job he had to sign more papers than they did at the Armistice! . . .

OK so they checked you out thoroughly. But then, what could you expect for five bob down and half a crown a week in those days. Even if the money had to be in by noon every Saturday on the dot. To be brutally frank, it wasn't unusual to see a man of my age racing down Buchanan Street to beat that mid-day deadline before the "heavies" moved in. I myself being a "prized" customer restricted myself to two suits with another one in reserve just in case I fell behind with the payments and the system. That way with the label still intact you could always swear it had never been worn. I reckoned it was a good security move in case that word "impound" reared it's ugly head. But fortunately for me nothing like that ever happened. And even to this day I doubt very much if my wife knew why I was so well turned out with suits. In a way that was but one of the pluses of having a foreigner for a wife I suppose. But whisper it . . .

It was just as well I'd spotted that advert because I now felt I was ready to face any potential employer or circumstance that fate threw at me. And it helped to build up my confidence again. And that could only be good for my own well being. Just as well, for shortly after that I was soon to be put to the test. I got a letter from British Railways stating that my application for a summer season job with them had been successful.

I was to report on Monday fortnight. My wife and I were really pleased. So pleased were we both that she let me go that Saturday to see the Celtic. It so happened that an Austrian girl friend was coming up to see her that Saturday afternoon. They had met when they'd lived round the corner from each other in Carntyne but weren't aware of it and were only getting to know each other when we moved. She had also married a Scotsman.

So as far as I was concerned things couldn't have panned out any better. I dressed conservatively in one of my C.W.D. tweed sports jackets and grey flannel trousers. But it was a mistake, for what I was about to witness was a travesty. I should have been dressed in all black to be on a par with what I was forced to watch on that football field. It was my team who should have been playing in all black. Whatever else they had done, Celtic had at least one thing to their credit. They had succeeded in perfecting mediocrity to their own image and likeness, and were now presenting it in a type of art form heavily disguised in those green and white hoops they were sporting.

And the jeers and shouts from the terracing echoed my sentiments as the supporters voiced their disapproval in no uncertain terms. Even the director's wives sitting up there in the comfort of the director's box got it too. And "The Jungle" was alive, but not with the sound of music. I had seen some bad Celtic teams in my day. But what hurt me most was that I had been through a war that had taken a heavy toll on me. A war that had brought me almost to the point of despair even insanity. And for what? To see my favourite team go down three goals to nothing to a team like Clyde?

The whistle for half-time came to Celtic's rescue so I wended my way to the vendor at the foot of the terrace just below "The Jungle" for my obligatory hot pie. I decided for once to forego the "P.K. A Penny The Packet" man. Just as I was about to take my first somewhat hesitant bite from my pie I accidentally overheard or perhaps I was meant to hear an even more sorrowful story being unfolded. It was being told in the past tense and was obviously not meant for younger ears. But hear it inadvertently or not, I most certainly did.

And sadly the saga told of a well known Celtic fan, a brewery worker by occupation who had managed to purloin a couple of experimental cans of beer from this famous brewery which were not yet on sale to the public. Not only were these cans destined to banish screwtop bottles to the scrap heap in the name of hygiene, but they would be much more compact. Sadly, the only thing those scientists had not yet perfected, was the "*easy-to-open*" ring-tops which later adorned the more sophisticated cans that were to follow.

Consequently, a can-opener or something similar had to be used to prise the can open. But revolutionary it most certainly was. Then tragedy struck. Call it foolhardy. Call it what you like the story-teller went on. But the fan in question, was setting himself up as a kind of guinea pig in the name of progress. And as such, had to be commended together with something else as it turned out. However, this particular fan it appears, had been imbibing well if not over wisely earlier on the contents of those pioneering cans. And up until then had encountered no difficulty whatsoever in slitting the top open with a can-opener.

But it was then seemingly, that events overtook him. The fan desirous of keeping his vantage point on a packed terracing and at the same time desperate to relieve himself had a difficult choice to make. Should he forego his dream spot on that terracing? Or should he go down to the urinals way below the terraces and there stand ankle deep in urine with the rest of the disciples, listen to "The Gospel According To Mathew and Daniel" and do it? Or should he stay put and improvise? Options! Options!

A decision was taken. And the consequences dire, the story goes. The said fan with a dutiful forewarning, it has to be said, of a "Jismineyirfeetaminitfillas," then thrust his manhood extension straight into the gash in the aforesaid can to let it all flood out, and in the can, as it were. Which it did.

Then perhaps by innocently dwelling on something or someone other than the game, he had an unexpected not to say unheralded erection. And in a matter of seconds that same fan was left on that terracing standing, with a very integral part of himself also standing inside that can with very little room for manoeuvre. Some cynics cruelly said later that it gave a whole new meaning to the phrase "*Standing* on the terracing!"

And the tale went on,.that the said imbiber who shall be nameless to protect the innocent as told by one of the stalwarts of the day who was there, panicked. And the more he panicked the worse the situation became and the more delicate his "position". For try as they may that awful day those helpers just couldn't separate that fan from that can!

Another terrace historian recalled how the game was forgotten. The more cynical thought it a pleasant diversion. But no one was laughing as volunteers wrestled somewhat unsuccessfully to "de-cant" that fan's manhood from that can. It was a situation that called for the utmost delicacy a trait hardly inherent in helpers whose team just happened to be getting beaten two goals to nothing at the time. But what to do for the best next was the question? To overdo the pulling could result in permanent damage to the victim not to mention the possible loss of what was still inside that can. "Just wait till he stops having a hard-on, and it might drap aff itself. "counselled One Wise Man From The East. Dennistoun to be exact. And you'll not get much further east than that!

White hankies it is written then began to flutter plaintively in the night air from high up on that terracing to try to catch the eye of the St John's ambulancemen. And it did. They raced up those terracing steps did those brave ambulancemen with their stretchers at the ready. And they say that there were mutterings amongst the multitudes as the sad spectacle was brought down on a stretcher. It is also reported that a plain simple white handkerchief had been draped respectfully over the "stress area", lest it caused offence.

And they do say that in the Royal Infirmary that very night that despite the application of soothing oils and the gentlest of massages by pretty nurses that the can remained firmly in place. The beer can just wouldn't come. Although it' was reported later, that the "victim" did. *Twice!* The doctors battled through the night, they say. Then a decision was taken. They would operate. A local anaesthetic would suffice. And the story ended, legend had it, with our hero going under but with a smile still on his face . . .

I didn't believe the story one little bit. And moved away with my hands cupped round my Bovril. There was quite a crowd of people round that storyteller. It was then that I formed the opinion as I'm sure many others would on reflection that the whole thing was a "come on" staged by Celtic to keep their supporters minds and thoughts away from their team. But the storyteller hadn't fooled me for a second. Celtic Football Club would never do a thing like that. Never! Would they?

I made my mind up never to go back again until they gave themselves a severe shake-up. But it wasn't just Celtic that had changed, Glasgow was beginning to change right in front of my very eyes. Glasgow, once famous for her landmarks was in danger of becoming a faceless place, a city without a past and a face without a future too, if something wasn't done about it quickly. But people would have to be prepared to fight back against the sort of changes that were threatening our way of life. And if they wouldn't fight them then I would.

No doubt about it, the death knell was already sounding for all those precious landmarks we'd all loved and grown up with. Then horror of horrors, newspapers were proclaiming that the old Glasgow had to go to make way for the new. But to people like me and many others things were moving too fast too soon. And there would be no redress for the bulldozers were beginning to move in with a vengeance. And from where I was standing or at least where I used to stand, one of the first that would be going, were those lovely little extremely amenable subterranean toilets. They had obviously been singled out as one of the first things to go. Was nothing sacred? I kept asking myself. However "redevelopment" like it or not was to be the "in" word then in the late fifties. But in my book it could well be marked down as one of the most heinous crimes of all time if those town planners were to get away with their ruthless plans.

But I saw no reason why they should. First of all it was the indecent haste with which it was all being done that incensed me. Those beloved little "bogs" were disappearing more or less overnight. But what to do, that was the question? Sadly no one else seemed to be worried about it. And it was all happening so fast. So fast that I began trying to keep count of just how many were being raised to the ground then filled in. And the result was staggering, almost one a night. and all in the name of this redevelopment thing. "redevilment" someone reckoned would have been a better name for it.

I decided to consult a local councillor and complain to him in the strongest possible terms about it all. But got nowhere. There were forty people in that surgery and thirty nine of them were only there because they wanted out of Drumchapel and they'd only been in Drumchapel a few weeks. Only one had any sympathy with my cause. Even the gaunt looking councillor gave me the impression he couldn't care less what happened to those little underground toilets. Come to think of it he looked the type who would rather wet himself than use a public toilet. And probably had . . .

There appeared to be no way of preventing the insidious march of those heartless bulldozers on those little helpless "bogs". I was convinced that there was some bureaucrat in George Square masterminding the whole thing. Possibly because he'd had a bad experience in the dim and distant past in one of them. Or maybe he'd been caught loitering with intent around one of them. A thousand curses on him. Despite all my efforts I'd decided mine was a hopeless task and braced myself for the worst. Prepared though I was, it was still a shock when I heard that yet another of these little landmarks was earmarked for closure. Horror of horrors again. It was none other than my own little favourite. A little pristine green railing job just outside the old "Kohinoor" pub in Dundas Street.

At first I refused to believe it. My eyes couldn't take it in? My immediate reaction was to petition the home secretary to have it reprieved or at the very least have it put back down the list a bit. For it was there many an evening or a Saturday afternoon after a beer or two that I would stand. And I would be properly positioned, legs apart, "extension" out, to enjoy a run off and savour the ambience of it all, and when completed the two statutory squeezes ( three and you were playing with it!) before slotting it away. Then looking up, you could see and hear the world scudding by through those little glass tiles that were inlaid into the pavement above. A sanctuary below ground for the common man. If ever there was one. It would be unthinkable to bury such a place. Just let them try I said to myself.

But try they did and succeed they did. Imagine if you will my horror once more on turning into Dundas Street one morning on my way to work. And there to find after a week or so writing to M.P.s up and down the country that I had to stop dead in my tracks. For there it was, or to be more exact, there it was not! My favourite little "bog" was no more. In it's place was a pathetic little mound of earth. Hardly an appropriate monument for such a sanctuary-like little oasis, was it?

But a far more disturbing feature I thought regarding the overnight bulldozing of those little toilets was one that disturbed me greatly. Were the appropriate warnings being given to those incumbents who may well have been downstairs during those final fateful hours? And if warnings were given were they given timeously? I kept asking myself. Those were the things that worried me then. Those were some possibilities that didn't bear thinking about. It may have been too soon then for such things as "the early warning system". But what I would liked to have known if even a perfunctory "All out" was even given . . . ?

For example an incumbent enthroned in his own little "arsenal" could well be just reaching out for a bog roll only to hear the ominous rumble overhead of a bulldozer up above him signalling the end. What a way to go! . . . My God. I thought to myself.

Those faceless men in George Square had a lot to answer for . . . Raaise those little underground establishments to the ground with a stroke of the pen they may. But what they and their kind didn't seem to appreciate was the basic needs they were depriving people of. People like myself and others. Especially when those people who just moments before had been enjoying the occasional "refreshment" in a nearby hostelry.

Then again, it may well have been that Glasgow Corporation had drafted in one of those daft sociologists to tell them how to run post-war Glasgow. And to see what else they could get rid off as well as the underground toilets. I myself could never ever understand those so called experts that were called in. And who could sit on a committee for about three years, then come up with such earth-shattering revelations like "Women over fifty were more liable to have earache after eating ice cream than a forty year old man". Or "People today eat 1 per cent more bread than a monkey eating a banana." All riveting stuff it may well have been. But would it do an awful lot for the ordinary punter caught short in the middle of Dundas Street at two o'clock in the morning and looking for an underground "bog". Would it?

To say that those Veritable Fountainheads of Useless Knowledge were ruining the country was putting it mildly. What they didn't seem to realise was that those same little downstairs "bogs." were educational as well as functional. Where else would you get those health notices for free that were always placed adroitly at eye level. I mean those notices that told the solid Glasgow citizen, or anyone else, the very street to go to should they have inadvertently copped a dose of the old "Opportunity Knocks". . . Where else, I ask you . . . ?

And not only that, what about those other handy little notices, like, " Please adjust your dress before leaving". which also gave you a sharp reminder before you raced up those hard stone little steps to the street. And what was nicer than to hear your cheery white-coated attendant, a cup of tea in his hand, shout out." Thank you, sir. Thank you for your custom. Drop in again sometime." " Change for the sake of change," I heard one such disgruntled punter moan before going on his un-merry way. And he was right. Because that's exactly what it was.

Plush flush toilets were emerging. No doubt dreamt up by our sociologist friends again. Away with the old and in with the new regardless of whether it worked or not. Why some of those new toilets even had paper towels. "That's what we're paying rates for," said another woman irately to her friend as they marched out. Not content with that in the early sixties they began to install those ( whisper it ) unmentionable machines. Loosely called "Buy Me And Stop One". Purely for the Randy Brigade. And for a little extra money they could get an Ultra Gossamer. Some were found wanting however. "Your Fucking Chewing Gum's Rotten." was written right across one such machine. No doubt put there by a dissatisfied customer.

If you thought for one moment that our sociologist friends had stopped invading our Toilets would be wrong.again. Terribly wrong. Unambiguous designations like, "Ladies" and "Gents" were to be consigned to the dustbins of history by our learned lavatorial friends in no uncertain terms. "Ladies" would now be substituted by a silhouette of a woman with legs apart and an impeccable figure. And "Gents" by a similar but very masculine silhouette with legs modestly closed. The very essence of sobriety and elegance.

Or was it the other way about with the legs that is . . . I still can't remember It's been so long! Pity, the poor Herbert however in those early days desperate for a pee. There he'd be and not having availed himself of a course on biology could quite easily have mis-read his silhouettes, and barged right in. Front Page cover in *The News Of The World* could well have resulted. Nor would it be difficult for a frustrated would-be journalist like myself to visualise the headlines that would follow: "Sex Mad Man Runs Amok In Glasgow's Ultra Modern Ladies Toilet."

My wife's English had improved tenfold. And that was one reason I stopped going to football matches. There were so many stories about fights and riots. And at that time, unheard of in Europe.

So it was no more Celtic for me. And anyway I was by then working most nights and at weekends in the local pub. And I was in my second summer season at Buchanan Street Station. My wife too had managed to get herself a job as a home help, which coincided with my two children starting school.

And by stint of working overtime in the railway a few times, and in the pub at nights I finally managed to get Hanni home to Flensburg for a short holiday. The next time I promised her the children would be with her. Things seemed to be picking up at last. I hadn't seen my brother Tam in ages. Maybe that's why things were going so well.

The last I'd heard of Tam he was driving double decker buses for Glasgow Corporation. He was on the Ruchazie to Croftfoot route, but was being pursued daily by the Bus Inspectors (The Gestapo). It had been reported that he was in the habit of taking the double decker home with him when he went for lunch, parking it outside the gate. Which was all very well. But he was so regular and so punctual every day that confused passengers thought that this must be a new terminus and started piling on to it at our gate. Starting A New Bus Route? That was Tam. He was nothing if not creative!

It was round about that time that my mother died. She had been ill for some time. We all had an inkling one way or the other that she was about to depart this earth. But the end when it finally came was nonetheless a shock to us all. We were all there at her bedside when those last moments came. The priest administered the last rites. Gave her extreme unction, which usually signals the end. And in keeping with those Catholic rituals and as though to obey God's Command to the last she turned her head to the side and died. She was and always had been a devout Catholic; and almost ninety when she died. A hard woman to boot. Stood no nonsense from anyone; except maybe from the wayward Tam.

My father never showed any emotion. But that didn't necessarily mean he would miss her any the less. But then again he wasn't the type given to outpourings of grief or anything like that. He would shed his tears in his own time. In his own presence. On the lighter side what he wouldn't miss was my mother's strict instructions from the living room window on how to handle those dahlias in the front garden. For my father like myself was no gardener. On occasions he was known to throw down the spade in disgust when those gardening instructions from my mother became too much for him. He would then go round the back, sit down on that old rustic seat we used to have, fold his arms and stay in the huff for hours.

Like myself, my father loved walking. He walked everywhere within reason. And even when the message from the king came to inform me of my award he would walk all over Carntyne showing it to everyone he knew. And even to some he didn't know. He was also astute enough to inform the local press and even succeeded in getting me a bit of publicity and my photo in the paper. He certainly believed in making the full use of his retirement years.

Not for my father sitting around waiting to die when he stopped. When he wasn't advising someone on superannuation matters a subject in which he was well versed he would be at a whist drive somewhere. That was another thing at which he was no slouch. A room full of canteens of cutlery and cartons of twenty-one piece dinner services, would bear testament to that. Hardly a week went past without him winning something or other. Curiously enough he wouldn't ever attend a whist drive where the prizes consisted purely of money. His contention being that money prizes always attracted the wrong type of players. That was my father. A man of many parts. Some of them hard. Some of them good. But none of them dishonest.

With the somewhat austere fifties behind us everyone appeared to take on a new lease of life. It may well have been that statement of the then Prime Minister Harold McMillan that did it. "You've never had it so good" he supposedly said although I myself had never heard him say it. But it seemed to work. For a while anyway. Jobs aplenty he kept telling us. And inflation was down. Expectations were high. So too were the expectations of some supporters that Saturday afternoon when I was at that Third Class window in Buchanan Street Station. And of course, it was just my luck that they happened to be Celtic supporters.

The station was jammed with those fans proudly sporting their traditional green and white scarves, and singing away as they awaited the arrival of "The Football Excursion Special" to Perth. The supporters were high because Celtic were chasing their tenth successive win in about five months. At long last they were getting better. And there was no one more pleased than myself as I doled out those tickets to those supporters of the team I loved. The "Special" train was due off at 12.42 p.m. from Buchanan Street Platform One, to arrive Perth 2.30 p.m. for the 3 o'clock kick off." The "Black Marias" ( where would we be without them?) were hovering discreetly outside. The din was deafening.

Then it all went wrong. First came the announcement over the tannoy. "Attention Please. Attention Please. Would passengers awaiting the arrival of the 12.42 train to Perth; please note that the train is running approximately forty minutes late at Stirling. We regret any inconvenience caused to passengers travelling to Perth.

Most especially to football fans travelling to Perth.This service has now been cancelled." Inside the booking office Mr Webster was almost beside himself as that same message was communicated to him by telephone. His face had gone ashen. It was almost half past twelve as it was.

Then he took over. "Close the windows. Stop issuing!" Another clerk at the other window and myself did just that. I could only hope no Celtic fan out there had recognised me. Because suddenly, and through no fault of my own I too, had become one of the enemy. For none of those fans out there were ever going to see that game. Never in a million years. Once more it was Action Stations, with Captain Webster at the helm.

" On the floor men. "Mr. Webster was already on the floor. The fans were banging on the wooden slats of the booking office. "Under siege. We're under siege. Excursions. Waste of time. Waste of money. Cost to company and life and limb too high." Mr Webster was back to his best Pitman's again. 200 words a minute at least I reckoned. But why the floor? I wondered.

Then it struck me. There was a large window on each side of the booking office, where members of the public could see in. And the public, in this case, were irate Celtic supporters. The phone went again and was gently pulled to the floor from it's standing position on the ledge above by Mr Webster. He listened intently then hung the receiver back on the hook. His face had now gone an even paler shade of grey, which I honestly didn't think was possible.

He beckoned the other clerk and myself over to him there as he knelt on the floor. So over we crawled. Mr.Webster gritted his teeth and clenched his fists as though he would have loved to have sworn but couldn't, being a Jehovah's Witness. However I got the impression he wouldn't have minded hiring someone to do it for him. And he was looking straight at me when he came off the phone. " Head Office. Immediate Refunds Not Poss. Got to go through usual channels. Grave. Very grave. Nonsensical system. Batten down hatches!!"

What Mr Webster was saying was that as those football fans wouldn't make it to the game they'd be wanting their money back. Which was perfectly true. And they would get it. But they would require to keep hold of their ticket and produce it next day before they could get their money refunded. But he doubted if they were prepared to wait that long as did I when I risked my head above the ramparts to steal a quick look out. Mr Webster had asked head office if instead they could make an immediate pay-out. This had been rejected. And so the hammering continued. Those fans wanted their money back and they wanted it now.

Mr Webster was still crawling up and down the booking office trying desperately to control events. But he did his crawling about in reverse by using his backside and his elbows. "Bad knees," he explained. He worked his way along the floor almost flat on his back and still using his elbows. He grabbed the phone and gave a number to the operator then waited trying to sit up as far as he dared without letting his head appear above that parapet again.

"H.Q? Webster here again. Situation desperate. Hemmed in. Siege situation. Office surrounded. Permission to refund. "He breathed out as best he could given the circumstances and awaited H.Q.s decision. The Celtic fans were hammering the windows now. But there was nobody to be seen. Everyone was on the floor. But it didn't stop then shouting and banging however. "Money back. Money back!" Mr Webster was visibly shaken." Language. Terrible." I could have told them that those Celtic supporters were capable of even more colourful swear words than that. But I decided not to . . .

Then Mr Webster got his reply as he lay back on the floor. A smile suddenly wreathed his face and he shouted down the phone. "Sensible decision. Sensible decision." He then hung the phone up and risked kneeling up. "Pay them out. But must produce tickets before refund. Fair's fair." He then stood up and reached under one of the ledges and produced a large cardboard box. It was crammed full of bars of chocolate. "Got these," he said "from the Fry's people. Services rendered." He then pointed to the cash drawers below the ticket windows. "Check tills!!" We checked tills. He then shouted out aloud. "Goodwill gesture to fans. Bars of Fry's chocolate. Two each with an apology for train cancellation. Go to it."

Give our Mr Webster his due. He opened the booking office door exited on to the platform and held his hands up to get a hearing from the angry shouting Celtic fans. The other booking clerk and myself held our breaths. It would never work, I thought. But it did. Miraculously it worked. The shouting got less and less. And our Mr Webster kept his head when he finally got the order he wanted. Cupping his hands to his mouth he shouted as hard as he could.

"Sorry lads about your train being cancelled. Engine failure. One of these things. Regrettable. Liked to have seen the game myself. Accept our apologies and a small gift for your children, if you have any, along with refund. Thank you. Line up please and get your money back. Better luck next time." He then smiled and waved, walked in the door and locked it hastily. "I didn't know you were a football fan, Mr Webster" I said, "let alone a Celtic supporter."

"I'm not," he said smiling. "Never saw a game in my life. Public Relations. Very important." The supporters lined up at the windows and were each handed their five bob refund back on production of their ticket. And each one received two bars of Frys chocolate along with their refund. When they were all paid out they began wending their way out of the station singing and shouting, "Are we down-hearted? No. No. No." The "Black Marias'" sirens whirled and whined, as they waited for"passengers". The cops stood beside their "Marias", arms folded and watched. Somewhat sullenly, I thought. But unfortunately for them that's all they managed. The supporters sang as they marched away good-naturedly. And even managed a little fortissimo as they passed that black van.

A situation that had looked irretrievably lost had just been rescued. And The Hero of the Day and of The Match that never was? There was no doubt as to who that was. It was none other than our very own Mr Webster and his bars of Fry's chocolate . . .

# Chapter Ten

*Barbers, Boozers and Bookies*

Glasgow's barbers were in a class of their own. I reckoned they were the best in Britain. I'd been in a few barbers in my day and they had all of them beaten. Their patter alone was unique. If you wanted the latest funny story your local friendly barber shop was the place to be. It was the hub. it was The Place. It was where it happened. There just was no other place. Once a month whether the cranium needed or not it, it had to be positioned under that white cover. Then and only then could you be sure you were really alive.

And every last Friday of the month it was a race to get down there and to await the delicate professional touches of those barbers. They were Entertainers. They were Advisers and they were Mediators. They were all those things, neatly packaged into white smocks with combs and scissors sticking out of their top pockets. Tell them a story they had never heard before and they would willingly even gleefully waive their usual tip. And sometimes just sometimes mind you they would give *you* a tip.

The Haircuts on the go in then in the sixties were "The D.A.," "The Tony Curtis", and "The Crew Cut". That is of course for those who had hair. For the hairless or the baldy bonces there was always the latest things in "Irish Jigs". Every taste catered for as they were at lengths to tell you. Then there were those topical tit-bits of the day with which they were most adept at using to their own advantage. I remember one time in particular.

It was in the sixties and Rangers were going through a bad spell having had about five managers in as many months trying to improve the team without success. Round about the same time communiques about the pope's health who was apparently in a bad way were being circulated daily. But that same day a further communique appeared which stated, "The Pope had a Good Night." The little barber who was doing my hair whispered in my ear. "What's the difference between Rangers and the Pope?" I raised my head as much as I dared. "I don't know. What is the difference between Rangers and the Pope?" He dusted me down, flashed the small hand mirror to the back of my head as they were wont to do then bent down and whispered in my ear, "The Pope's getting better!" He then whipped the white sheet away from me with a flourish and smiled through the large mirror smile at me. "I think you 'll find that to your liking, sir . . . "

But those little barber shops were beginning to feel the pinch too, just like their underground toilet counterparts. The bulldozers were looming for them as well. Especially the smaller barbers shops who were finding it difficult to expand.

Those nice little red and white poles were on their way out if those Civic Fathers or whatever other ridiculous name they were given ever got their way. One such councillor was reputed to have called those little poles, "A blot on the landscape". He was probably drunk on leaving the City Chambers after having stuffed himself on a three-course lunch at the taxpayers expense at the time.

Because make no mistake about it. Those so called councillors were the real blots on the landscape. They were the real parasites. If they bought a bar of chocolate on the way home you can bet your boots it went on their expense account. And probably wanted those little barber shops pulled down so that new plush salons could be built. They would then get the job of opening them with the possibility of a fee and a free haircut into the bargain.

Everything was to be sacrificed in the name of progress. But then graffiti started rearing it's ugly head. It was everywhere. They reckon it had even made it to the Sheriff Court. Right above the judge's head. "Justice Rools." It was good to know that the "artist" had completed his course on "English", before embarking on his expedition to save the world from injustice.

Glasgow was going mad all of a sudden. The war was well and truly behind us. And it was to the future we must now look. Shaken off were the austerity and the shortages and the skimping of the fifties. Everyone was going to be a millionaire. It was within everyone's grasp we were told. Certainly work was plentiful. My wife and my family were doing well. Hanni had managed over to Germany to see her folks. And everything in the garden at that very moment looked lovely.

Then of course it all happened. In the midst of life as they say my father died. It was a case of the heart outstripping the body I fear. Because my father was an energetic man who as I said before walked everywhere. He was ninety years of age, and survived a couple of strokes prior to his death. His heart could probably have lasted another ninety years. But it was his turn to go. And he was never a man to have asked for any special favours from God or from anyone else come to that. Once again we all managed to be there at his bedside. A few months before his death he was told by the doctor to give blood as he had a tendency to high blood pressure. This he did with relish. And typical of the man, my father started drinking a glass of Guinness to offset the demands on his blood. Although prior to that he had been a lifelong teetotaller

To this day we never ever found out why my father left County Cavan in Ireland to come to Scotland. There were varying stories regarding his exit from Ireland before surfacing in Rutherglen in the eighteen eighties. One story had him being found drunk in a ditch somewhere in Ireland where he'd been a postman. A sack of undelivered letters apparently lay beside him in the ditch. And all this seemingly resulted in him fleeing from his native Ireland in shame. This story was never ever corroborated to this day. Nor denied for that matter.

Another story had it that he originally wanted to go to Liverpool but got on the wrong boat at Dublin. But that story got short shrift from some of my Irish cousins. So one must lean somewhat to the former story. One thing was for certain. He met my mother in Rutherglen and there they were married. He hadn't been a big earner in his day. Glasgow Corporation Water Department wasn't exactly known then for it's high wages. But despite all this he still managed to save a bit. And when his will was read out we were all pleasantly surprised to find he had left one hundred pounds to each and every one of us. And that then was a lot of money.

The only ones then left in Carntyne were my eldest sister who had never married and Tam. The rest of us had moved on. Tam had survived another *COUP DÉTAT* by those bus inspectors to oust him as a bus driver, but then he managed to get the union behind him and subsequently foiled them once more. Then biding his time, he finally left and went back to long distance lorry driving again. I had successfully served my two years apprenticeship with British Railways and was now a fully-fledged railwayman at Sighthill Freight Terminal up in Glasgow's Springburn. The old High Street and College Street Goods Depots had now been closed and were now all under the one umbrella of Sighthill Freight Terminal

Everything was brand new. Nothing had been spared. Stainless steel and aluminium abounded. Large inter-communicating offices with large windows were set above the railway lines and the freight trains and the loading bays. It was a huge complex. Second only in size to London St Pancras. The siting of the loading bay was unfortunate, to say the least. For looking down from a street above residents could hang out of their windows and watch the loading and the unloading of the goods from freight trains on the freight yard below.

And of course as Christmas neared the temptation got even greater. It became a standing joke. So exposed were those goods stacked out there in the open, that one could envisage a Glasgow housewife hanging out of her vantage point window with her young son pointing and saying. "What would you like for your Christmas, son?" And the youngster pointing down. "I'd like that bike, Ma." "And you'll hiv it son, you'll hiv it. Your da will go doon this very night and get you it." The losses the first year were astronomical. The freight yard was wide open. Unfortunately the eyes of some of those residents on the street above were wider still. And as long as I was there until the mid- seventies the situation had never been resolved.

Bustling Springburn was a place and a half too. With it's fair share of pubs and betting shops and dogs. And not necessarily in that order. But it was the only place where I could honestly say that I saw a dog take a woman for a walk. A huge Alsatian dog was literally pulling it's minder along the pavement one day. The woman was on the small side it should be stressed. But she seemed to be quite happy when one of our yard workers tried to go to her rescue. "Mind your ain bloody business," she said to him. "It's just that his legs are that bit longer than mine and he goes that bit quicker!"

Springburn also had it's fair share of those little butcher's shops with the sawdust still on the floor. and half a sheep's carcass strung up as you went into the shop and where the occasional dog would have no hesitation sometimes in cocking a leg up and having a run off against it. And nobody seemed to mind. "The dugg's no daein oanybody any harm and the sheep's deid anyway." The new hygiene laws had just came into force. And butcher meat was top of the list. And what did they do those butchers who were under the cosh in the sixties? "Now Wash Your Hands." was the notice posted in most food shops, including those well-known Grocer Henrys who sold those great jet black rolls that were great with butter.

But it didn't make a great deal of difference then in the late sixties. Some shops still had sawdust on the floor and it had been noticed that in some shops a slice of raw beef ham or a piece of chopped ham and pork had been shoved back on the shelf after hitting the sawdust. But to be fair it should be noted that after replacing it back on the shelf the assistant did wash his hands and would even put on his little white hygienic hat if you asked him nicely. Those that were issued after the hygienic clamp down that is. Even the throwing of the mince on to the scales was being carefully monitored. And in some shops they had a notice for the benefit of dogs pinned on to their strung up sheep. And it said: "Keep Off."

I well remembered reading that Glasgow had more pubs to the square mile than any other city in Europe. Just how they came to that conclusion I shall never know. And no, I hadn't worked in them all. It just felt like it sometimes. Nor was it down to devotion or anything like that. It was due to necessity and nothing more. Married men like myself, had to work most nights, and most week-ends to make up for the lack of decent wages in our day jobs. It most certainly wasn't for pin money or anything like that.

Even in Glasgow in those early days counterfeit money was still illegal and just as hard to make. Not only that but even in those pre-securicor days banks too, were just too difficult to rob. And that despite the fact that money from banks was openly transferred from barrows crammed full of the stuff in broad daylight; the stocking mask hadn't been thought of then. Otherwise, more "hard men" may have had a go. So for myself, and others built like me who just weren't cut out physically for crimes of violence; it had to be the hard slog, and that meant a job behind the bar in a pub doling out oceans of booze to Glasgow's insatiable hordes, or starve to death.

Embedded in my head for ever would be the memory of the first pub I ever started in way back in the late fifties. It was halfway up the Garscube Road in Glasgow's North Side. A great barn of a place it was. I would never forget it. If they starred pubs then like they star hotels and pubs now it would have rated five. Not five stars. I mean *five nothings.* For example if a fiver was ever handed over the counter it was first of all held up to the light about four times. After that it warranted a quick sureptitious phone call to the head pub further up the road. After that it would be witnessed by all the bar staff swearing on a bible before being finally accepted and hitting the "Jack and Jill".

It was that kind of pub. Hardly a tavern for the discerning. It transpired however that I had become enmeshed into the Official Headquarters of Glasgow's "King Lear and MacBeth" men. So honoured, I discovered later because of it's unique geographical link. In other words it was bang next door to a common close that still had gas mantles on the landings. And even better next door again there was a dairy. So it was a case of the methylated spirit, the milk and up the close for the "flavouring". Then back into the pub again to wash it all down with the cooler stuff. You could say that that particular pub was a kind of tactical H.Q . . .

Then it gradually hit me. I'd got the job because nobody else wanted it. And there was me thinking it was my appearance and my talents that had won the day for me. Silly me. "You'll get one and six an hour. Your shop drink will be a pint during the week. And on a Saturday you'll get a half and a half pint, or a packet of fags. It's up to you." The word Saturday had been heavily underlined. So any ideas I'd previously entertained about having any mid week orgys behind the bar up in the Garscube Road I could forget it. It would appear that if there were to be any "knees up" nights it would be confined to Saturdays only. Not only that but I'd just had it confirmed that as well as being a "King Lear" pub it was also reputed to be a "Hun Hostelry". Now I knew why I'd been started. They knew it could well mean that there could be one "Tim" less at the Celtic end in the very near future! So it was to be a double-edged sword. Either way I couldn't win. But they could. We'd soon see about that I thought. Create a diversion which I did one night. "Look," I shouted pointing to the door. "Looks like an accident out there!"

The big "Bluenose" chargehand turned his head to look and I quickly annexed forty Capstan from the gantry and stuffed them up my apron. He turned his head back quicker than I anticipated "What's that?" he snarled. "What's what?" I asked innocently. "Up your apron" he hissed back his big chin jutting out like the gangway going out from *The "Waverley"* docking at Dunoon. "Up your apron too," I shouted back my heart pounding. "Can I not get scratching myself?" I replied quickly. "W-Well do it in your own time after this," he said back-tracking. There won't be any next time if I can help it I remember thinking.

The whole thing came to a head one night. I had been behind the bar from six o'clock and had only served two customers. And one of them had only been looking for change of a pound. It was then that two "sartorial" types entered. There was obviously a very strong bond between them for they were supporting each other. I immediately dubbed them "Bill and Ben The Methyl Men". They made it albeit somewhat tentatively to the bar. "Two glesses." Arms folded I looked them straight in the eye which wasn't easy I hasten to add for those eyes were rolling. "Two glesses o' whit?" I asked just to let them know that even if I wasn't an incumbent I could speak the lingo . . .

On getting no reply I looked along the bar at Billy minus his crown for guidance. He nodded assent. Economics were forcing his hand. "O.K. then whit yiz wantin'?" I asked. "Two glesses o' wine and two hauf pints," came the reply. We could only hope they both had money for above my head across the gantry adroitly placed was a large sign which said. "Please Do Not Ask For Credit As A Refusal Often Offends." It seemed to work, for a few coins rolled along the counter. I managed to salvage the appropriate amount and pushed the rest back to them. "We're not allowed to accept tips," I said sarcastically . . .

Both our two worthys then managed back to their seats and were soon draped around their drinks. I walked up and down the inside of the bar and looked around the other side. The whole left side of the bar was absolutely empty. There wasn't a mark on the sawdust. Apart from our two lavish spenders in the corner it was virtually virgin territory. Big Billy had a perplexed look about him. I got the impression he was trying mentally to recall just how many twenty packets of Capstan he'd stocked that morning up in the gantry and just how many he had actually sold. "Be back in a minute," he said. Not only was he tight with his money. He rationed his words too. He then opened the flap of the cellar and disappeared down closing it behind him as he went under.

He was only under about five minutes. The moment he surfaced he looked across to where our only customers had been seated. "Where are they?" he cried pointing over to where stood four empty glasses but no Bill and Ben.

"I don't know. They must have gone to the bog." "What?" he roared. He then raced round to the other side of the bar and headed for the Gents. He then re-appeared almost immediately holding one imbiber by the scruff of the neck with one hand and the other similarly with the other. He almost carried them to the door. And their feet were not touching the floor. I'd swear to that. "Now I don't want to see either of you in here again," he shouted to them as they folded into a heap on the pavement outside.

He then shouted to me when he entered. "Right. Get me plenty of brown paper. You'll find some under the counter." So I looked and found some. "Hurry up before they stink the place out." I found some and handed it over. "Right. You stay there and mind the shop. I'll be back in a few minutes. Later I saw smoke billowing out of the Gent's toilets. I raced round to get Billy to raise the alarm.

Instead he was kneeling down fanning the flames. "You'd better watch what you're doing," I said. "I know thing's are bad Billy but the insurance people are not going to fall for that one You'd better get that fire out and quick." "No. No," he said. "You don't understand. It's the Meth. The only way to kill the smell is to burn brown paper. You see that's why you daren't let them have a pee. When their urine hits the air the mixture of the urine and the Meth gives off a toxic odour when released into the atmosphere. I remember reading about it. That's how I know. You shouldn't have let them go to the toilet. So you shouldn't." I marvelled for a moment at big Billy's scientific knowledge even although he was a' Ger supporter And almost told him so. But decided against it.

"So it's all my fault then, is it?" I said. "No," he said abruptly. "It's both our faults. Me for letting you serve them. And you for letting them go to the bog." I was a little surprised by Billy's magnanimity and was about to say so when he spoiled it all by sighing and shaking his head. "Of course, the worse crime of the two was committed by you for letting them into the bog in the first place, if you don't mind my saying so," he said

"How do you mean?" I asked puzzled. Then he pushed a cubicle door open and pointed to the wall. "Didn't check for crayons did you?" he said wryly. "Crayons?" I asked, my brows furrowing. "Yes crayons," he said, pushing the toilet cubicle open even further and pointing to the wall. There in bold red capitals on the wall was a hand-penned poem for all to read.

There was An Old Woman of Kilkenny
Who gave you a feel for a penny
For a half of that sum
You got touching her bum
For a farthing you didn't get any.

"Slipped through your fingers again. Didn't he?" That had me puzzled. "Who slipped through who's fingers?" I asked "The BARRED BARD of the Bog. that's who. He's called THE BARRED BARD because he's barred from every pub in Glasgow because of his dirty poems. Oh I'm not blaming you entirely. He could have been disguised. But it's obvious that you're not from this side of the city. Otherwise you would have checked. We both should."

I didn't have the heart to take him for any more fags, King Billy or no King Billy. So I had my shop drink. Then he gave me another and we Toasted The Barred Bard. And shut up shop. I never set eyes on him again. I didn't do any more work behind bars after that. And instead swore to restrict myself to the other side of the city.

Glasgow like many other big cities had her fair share of betting shops. And again where you had a pub you had a betting shop adjacent. And they were works of art those present day shops. A very far cry from what they were in the old days. All the furtiveness of the fifties had gone together with the guilt that went with it. Not to mention, the ever constant threat of the law.

Because betting was illegal in the early days. And it was not unusual for "The Hurry-up," van to come hurtling round a corner, run into a bookies and empty the human contents into the back of the van and off to the "Pokey". And there all would be confined till a fine was paid. Which to be fair was always paid by the bookie. But despite all those benevolent overtures punters became frustrated and maintained it was affecting their concentration. And things were never the same.

Then, to the rescue, came the Betting and Gaming Act. Gambling was made legal. A man could now lose his money with impunity. Gone for ever were the days when boys had to scurry up a back close to give some humphy-backed little man a sixpence, accompanied by a "line frae ma faither". No longer was your local betting shop a grotty little hut liable to be raided at any moment. Almost overnight your local betting shop was transformed into a bright fluorescent lit saloon, with beautifully upholstered leather seats and cushioned chairs. Even writing desks and ledges and free ball-point pens were also on hand to assist you on your downward trend.

And in those sanctums you would now find as beautiful and as well endowed a bevy of damsels as you'd find anywhere to attend to all your needs. Your betting needs that is. Yet some people had the nerve to call them "Dens of Iniquity"! Rubbish. Nothing could be further from the truth. As a matter of fact everything had suddenly became much more pleasant. It was all so civilised now. Mind you it didn't make picking the winners any easier. But a look over the counter at some of those long legs that were taking your money somehow made it that little bit more bearable.

Not only that. But even if you couldn't back a winner you could always walk out of that particular shop with your pockets bulging with ball- point pens ripe for flogging. No strip-searches there as you headed for the exit door. Those much maligned bookies were performing a public service; fulfiling a much needed want just like their little underground toilet predecessors. And let's not forget that your modern betting shop had atmosphere as well as stale cigarette smoke. Not only that but it was a jolly place to be and don't let anyone tell you to the contrary. Especially if you were winning. Or when the "favourites" were romping home to shouts of "Go on ya beauty!"

They were comfortable places. And it was shelter from the rain and the cold especially if your own electricity had been cut off. Successive Tory governments were very quick to acknowledge the importance of the betting shop and its place in Glasgow's not inconsiderable betting circles. The astute Tories had done their homework and discovered that some Glasgow folk stayed longer in betting shops than they did in their own homes. So they set about solving the housing problem by building more betting shops!

The moment a grocer or a butcher shop folded it was a pretty safe bet that it would surface again as a, Yes, you've guessed it . It opened up as a betting shop. Predominantly in working class districts like Springburn, Bridgeton or Shettleston of course. So much so that in those early days some of those same districts were in danger of becoming bereft of any kind of shops whatsoever. Small wonder then, that often the "mince" money went on a "Yankee" or a "Three Cross bobs and a bob up the side" bet. In some cases it was the only way to shop!

I liked a bet myself and still do. But only for the "thrill of the chase" as we all say. Certainly not for the money. My wife would certainly subscribe to that. Now and again I would ask her for the loan of a "Billy the Kid" on a Saturday. (Yes. She did know what the Glasgow slang for a quid was.) But I seldom got it. I suppose I would be classed as a moderate gambler. Which meant that when I did win I didn't win a lot. But conversely and most importantly when I did lose and it was often it wasn't the end of the world.

The betting shop of today would not be the same if it wasn't for the tipster. He was the Herbert that always got it "good". The tip that is. He would bore everyone rigid about the impeccable sources from whence this "information" came . . .

It went without saying that this info was very restricted. Lips sealed and all that. And "whispers" to be kept strictly within the environs of a few friends . . .

What it boiled down to was that this Herbert supposedly knew a bloke who was married to another bloke who's sister used to live next door to Jenny Pitman's uncle and the pony in question just had to turn up at the track. It just had to be there to win. The sad feature about the tipsters of that day was despite all this information his appearance was the very antithesis of what he should be. His shirt tail would usually be hanging out of the back-side of his trousers. And that was on a good day when he was "properly" dressed.

The ramifications of all this hush-hush stuff usually proved to be even more disastrous as far as the betting shops were concerned. Even though the recipient of a hot tip was usually sworn to secrecy he or she usually succumbed under pressure and nine times out of ten spilled the beans eventually. And in a matter of minutes it was all over the place. Consequently you had punters walking up and down the shop whispering out of the corners of their mouths to each other. Some shielding their lips with a newspaper were also twisting the corner of their mouths as they passed one another. And very soon nearly everybody was talking out of the corner of their mouths. So much so that the only ones who weren't talking out of the corner of their mouths and not facially afflicted were the bookies themselves. But then what would they know? They were only taking the money . . .

The carbonised betting slip was another revolution of it's day when it arrived in the late sixties. It saved a lot of time and effort on the part of the punter and made his lot an easier one. Prior to that a punter had to write his bet on an ordinary single piece of paper and hand it in to the bookie who in turn would give you a receipt. But this receipt was usually just an ordinary receipt which confirmed that you had actually placed a bet.

As was the case then, a punter kept his own check of the horses he had backed and usually had a nom de plume he would use known only to him which he would declare when handing over his receipt. It was a safeguard against anyone trying to usurp your winnings. Notwithstanding there was a story doing the rounds about a punter apparently the worse of drink going up to the bookie to collect his winnings one day. Then after searching his pockets he confessed to the bookie that he'd lost his receipt. "Well, sir, can you remember your non de plume?" the bookie asked. This remark brought a look of askance to the somewhat confused punter. "Nom de Plume? . . . Nom de fuckin' plume is it? How should I know . . . ? I nivir goat French at school . . . Jist haun' over the money pal or else . . . !"

Oh yes. The betting shops both Ancient and Modern had many hymns to sing. And they weren't all about hymns of praise either. But they had their crosses to bear too did those bookies. Especially on what was called a "Low News" day. That was a term used by newspapers when stories were thin on the ground. However that old sanitised saying about no news being good news just did not apply this particular day.No news was very bad news. But "A No Racing Day" was even worse news. More so when greyhounds and any animals that actually had legs and could race but couldn't race. Now that really spelled disaster.

Such was the case one such morning when I happened to pop in to my local friendly betting shop just to see how everyone was going to get through the day without losing money. The loyal few that were there were grouped around *The Sporting Chronicle* desperate to fund out when racing was liable to be on again after days of incessant rain. Each one had that funereal look about him. The headline in *The Chronicle* that race-free day was *"Well Known Bookie Dies At Seventy Four."* As I turned to head for the exit door I heard one punter say to another bitterly. "The bastard. I thought you would have got at least *2/1* about him at least, never mind *7/4!"* . . .

"Alcoholics Anonymous" or "Gamblers Anonymous." Call them what you will. I myself neither won nor lost either way at the ponies. And that was not due to any prudence on my part. It was due mainly to the fact that I never had enough money at any time to do anything with. It was then I decided to give myself a classification which other people like myself could well be labelled. The "In Betweens". Therefore I and my ilk from here on in should quite rightly in my opinion be known as "Gamblers Synonymous". Roughly speaking we would-be punters who liked to gamble but didn't have enough money to lose. Curiously enough my big brother Tam had hardly ever set foot inside a betting shop. A pub yes. But never The Bookies. To Tam it was simply a waste of good drinking money. And who would argue with that? The doctor, maybe . . . And the last time I had seen Tam he was really hitting the booze hard. In fact a few years before he died every one of us, especially his daughter told him that if he didn't cut out the booze dramatically it could spell the end of his life. And surprisingly the usual stubborn Tam appeared to have got the message and promised to give up the drink.

And he did give it up for a few months. Which was just as well for the dreaded breathalyser had become a reality. If ever our Tam needed a reminder it was that. Another great Celtic man like myself he had his own particular clique of three who all went to the game together. Tam was the driver. Not only because he was the owner of the said jalopy at that time but because he knew the routes to all those away games. And being in the haulage business not to mention other "businesses" he knew how and where to park and how to confuse the "noseys" when ever the occasion demanded it And it often did. His "passengers" trusted him implicitly with the petrol money etc etc. Like I say they trusted him. They had to. He was all they had.

One Saturday in particular my informant tells me Tam as usual drove his consorts to Tynecastle to see them play the Hearts. British Rail were doing a big thing around that time, publicity wise. "B.R. Will Take You There And B.R. Will Take You Back." Well Tam was already doing all these things without any publicity whatsoever up until then I was told. And his mouth had been alcohol-free for about four months.

He was then drinking nothing stronger than pure grape juice, supposedly a great alcohol simulator which he admitted later he quite liked. But that old song about "Does Your Chewing Gum Lose It's Flavour On The Bedpost Overnight" was also doing the rounds. It would prove to be prophetic and thereby hangs the story. Tam the quintessentially Sobersides as he was that day had driven his "disciples" all the way from Glasgow on a very wet Saturday afternoon. And throughout the journey those chosen ones were singing their heads off as they lolled about in the back. They had been looking on the real stuff when it had been very red indeed. A testing time for Tam. It was then that something in Tam snapped.

Not only had he got them there. He'd managed to get parked then guided them to the ground. But they were still singing and dancing despite the presence of mounted policemen obviously there to martial the crowds. And those uniformed cowboys were determined to get all supporters to drink up before entering the ground or leave it behind. For that was the new law. "Drink it or sink it." And those formidable hoofs looked ominous as they reared up in front of Tam as he stood there with his bottle of *pure grape juice.*

All around him other discerning imbibers were emptying beer and whisky down their respective gullets rather than "waste" it before they went in. That they say is when Tam lost it, together with his zest for grape juice. A certain uniformed latter day Roy Rogers looked down from his mount on high on Tam and his bottle of juice. "Drink it!" he thundered baton raised, horses, hooves hovering reinforcing him to the full. Tam looked up. Looked at the bottle of juice then thrust the bottle upwards emphatically toward the mounted enforcer. "No, You fucking drink it!" Suddenly the mountie's horse reared up and unseated his jockey, (like they say in best racing parlance). And all hell was let loose in Gorgie Road as horses mounted or un-mounted were all cavorting about searching desperately for a non-alcoholic alcoholic . . .

After that they tell me Tam laid the law down to his followers. There would be no more taxi service to Celtic Park or any other park until the boozing in the back stopped. In other words, if Tam was driving and not drinking nobody was drinking. It was as simple as that . . .

It wasn't all that long afterwards that poor Tam died despite a belated effort on his behalf to stop drinking. And he really did try. But the damage to his liver had been extensive. He was philosophic about the whole thing curiously enough. Not for him a lot of soul-searching and self pity. Instead he was a cheery patient whilst in hospital. I went up one night to visit him. Outwardly he was his usual self. But deep down you got the impression he knew only too well that he hadn't long to go. I promised to go up and see him again. But the visit never materialised. He died the next night. so I never really got the chance to say goodbye. Thus it was farewell to Tam and to all those various escapades. He may not have been the ideal husband for a woman. But whatever he did he did it. And he feared no one. No one knew that more than myself. I didn't know what particular heaven he would be going to. But I knew God wouldn't have wanted him in Hell. For God knew fine well that Tam would have been wasted in Hell. There was plenty for him to do in other places . . .

Tam never managed to live long enough to see the introduction of decimalization. He would have loved all the hype that accompanied it's arrival though. There were Talk-Ins everywhere. In the Workplace. In the Shops. Even in the bookies the resident punters were shown how a three cross double and a bob up the side became translated into a three cross five pence double and five pence up the side. Some of the punters were bemused by the whole thing. "It's a nice change, mind you," one punter reputedly remarked to another. "But I cannae see it lastin'. If you know what I mean."

But last it did. Even in Henry's; Glasgow's renowned grocer famous for those black scrumptious rolls shoppers were having trouble coming to terms with this latest phenomenon. Those loyal customers were puzzled by the whole thing and were beginning to have doubts about decimilization's place in modern society, especially Glasgow's. No one. But no one ever doubted that Henry's black rolls filled with with a quarter of lamb's tongue, or a tasty slice of chopped ham and pork weren't good value. Of course they were. Tantalisingly displayed if somewhat precariously on glass ledges in those little white Doyley's they were, and always would be irresistible but could they all survive decimalization? That indeed was the question.

Therein lay the trouble with those loyal buyers of black rolls, chopped ham and pork and boiled bacon. "Why can't they just leave things as they are?" said one as she queued up there in the sawdust of Henry's in the Saltmarket. "Change for the sake of change, that's all it is Isa." "Aye your right there." "I blame The Common Market for it all," said another. "All these cents and marks are all right for the foreigners. They're no' for us." "Aye and another thing aboot this Common Market. We just don't have the weather for it. You'll no' get me buying stuff that's been oot on the pavement all day. Especially sausages. Oor weather's jist no clement enough for it so it's no'."

No question about it. The natives just weren't happy with decimilization. One little pirate butcher in Springburn even put the proverbial cat amongst the pigeons by refusing point blank to join The Decimilization Club. Not only that he vowed to keep his butcher meat products at the old L.S.D. prices of one and sixpence a pound for the mince and two bob for the stewing steak. They reckon he was last seen between a sandwich board walking up and down the Springburn Road denouncing decimilization mince as having no taste whatsoever. In his shop in Springburn a sign in the window read, "Only Non Decimal Mince sold here." And he also employed a man to parade up and down the street with a sandwich board which said it all. "BY NON. BUY NOW"

Glasgow was the fun city of Europe as far as I was concerned. Not just in Britain. You just had to walk along Argyle Street any day at any time to see that. There was a buzz about Glasgow that you didn't get from any other city except perhaps for London. Was it not Glasgow that was nominated as the City Of Culture in 1990? Where else indeed would you go if you wanted a "daud" of culture?

# Chapter Eleven

*The Way It Was*

Being the baby of the family in those early days of the nineteen twenties had it's advantages. I was born in November 1917. My oldest brother Johnny had been born some fifteen years earlier. This meant that he had left school and indeed had started work even before I was born. Presuming of course that there was work to be had round about that time. Because work was scarce then. And the jobs that were around would bring howls of laughter and disbelief to our younger generation today. In fact one of the first jobs Johnny had on leaving school was testing eggs of all things to see if they were fresh or not. And how was that done in the twenties in Downtown Calton?

First of all it had to be done in daylight because electric light if there was any then did not run to extensions. The tester would then sit round the back of the egg store and hold each egg up in turn to the light. And that light more often than not was by candle. If the tester could see through the shell on to the light the egg was good. Needless to say the tester didn't always need to look through the shell because the smell emanating from the egg itself would often indicate that it was unfit for human consumption. It would then be discarded into an overflowing bucket of rotten eggs that stank to high heaven and permeated the entire area. My brother only stuck the job three weeks he told me. And went off eggs for about three years after that.

There was another job around about that time for very strong young men. And that job would be to assist older men to help get horses back on their feet again after they had fallen down in the road, true in those days the roads were cobbled or very loosely tarred resulting in many of those loveable old Clydesdale horses slipping and falling to the ground in pain . . . Weighing well over a ton when those Clydesdales went down believe me they stayed down. And they would just lie there till someone managed to get them to their feet again.

Those old Clydesdales weren't stupid by any means. They knew fine well that the longer they stayed lying down the shorter their day and that would mean less heavily laden carts they would have to pull later on. One got the impression that they were staunch believers of that old army maxim. "When you're marching, you're not fighting." I'd swear I saw one of them winking a very large eye at me as it lay there peacefully head resting on the pavement awaiting the erectors with their lassos and ropes etc . . .

Those erectors were usually composed of two men, sometimes three. Often I'd watch them go through their paces as they cajoled and wrestled to get those great gentle giants to their feet with the aid of their ropes. But they weren't always successful not by any means and the drill was always the same. A rope would be thrust around the harness, a large rope around the horse's midriff and a large steel rod to slip under the back to give it some sort of lift. And the police were always there, whether as spectators or just to see that there would be no cruelty to the animal we knew not. But they were always there truncheons and all.

It was then just a case of let action commence. And it inevitably did. There would also be a bale of hay there as a special attraction. The rope would be pulled steadily but tightly by two strong men with a third ready to slide the pole under the horse to ease it upwards. Then with one concerted move all those skills would be applied on a given signal. This signal was invariably given by the police and before you knew it the horse would be on it's feet again. Significantly however this was not always the case.

Often a horse would be fully aware that he was the main centre of attraction as he lay there. Of this I am certain, and sometimes that same horse would rebel and decide to sit back on his haunches when only halfway up and survey the scene in a somewhat theatrical fashion. This would immediately bring gasps of consternation from the onlookers thinking that something had gone wrong and that the horse had injured himself in some way on the way up.

But it all could have been a ploy by a very roguish horse. Who's to know? So many falls. So many horses. Another pull on those ropes and another grey flecked beauty could be finally on her feet at last. All this to thunderous applause from those spectators who were constantly being pushed backwards by the police. For make no mistake about it, this was Street Theatre at it's finest. In fact, in many cases it was the only theatre available to the poor people of the Calton or any other part of Glasgow in those days.

The saddest thing of all however was when a horse had a particularly nasty fall and could not get to her feet at all. The vet would be called and crowds would stand silent with due reverence and watch as the limited equine skills of the twenties were administered to the stricken animal. Sadly too those medical shortcomings would often result in the animal having to be put down. Because drugs and cures were scarce enough for humans let alone animals in those early days. Hushed consultations between helpers and police would then ensue. Then and only then would the crowds be asked to disperse. Which they would do, but only to go around the corner where they would wait because they knew that a horse was about to die in their very midst.

The dull but distinctive sound of a pistol shot would follow. Then an even more marked silence, and on many occasions a tear, for this was a sudden death albeit of an animal, but it was almost as grievous as a sudden death in the family. Because at that time horses in particular were even more susceptible to sudden death than we humans. Fatalities on the road for human beings were few and far between simply because the only forms of transport around that time were trams, and buses. And trams could always be heard well in advance. Buses too only travelled at about twenty miles an hour giving a person plenty of time to get out of the road. But nothing alas to warn an old horse of an impending fall.

The Ice Man Cometh. Oh yes. And cometh he came often. For the coming of those lorries carrying great blocks of ice were another feature of my boyhood. I would often stand and wonder at the size of those blocks of ice. Frozen Water. For that's what it was. What an invention they were. Those huge block of ices would be pushed off the lorry on to the pavement and then dragged into the fishmongers by means of two massive iron claws pulled by an equally massive man wearing a waterproof apron. Sometimes, slivers of the stuff would splinter our way and we would grab a piece and shove it straight into our mouths without any hesitation whatsoever. For this was instant refreshment. It was the ice lolly of the day and very acceptable too, especially in the summertime and all for nothing! Whatever next, I often wondered.

Voting day was another momentous time for me when I was a very young child. And I often wondered why people didn't have voting days more often. We were all to have better homes and more to eat. Because that's what it said on the posters and on the leaflets that were pushed through our doors. There was to be no more unemployment; for everyone would have a job. There would be more money to spend on clothes and food and holidays. Because that's what it said on the posters and the leaflets. Every home should have a garden where we could all play. And we were going to get it. Everything was going to be a whole lot better. Because that's what it said on the posters and the leaflets. And I believed. "For when I was a child I believed and spoke as a child."

Men with flowers in their buttonholes were giving us sweets and apples and oranges. Even the horses which pulled the carts, had garlands of flowers round their necks. Everywhere there were flowers. We were told to jump up on the carts by the men and they would take us all the way to Glasgow Green or even as far away as Bellahouston Park if we sang their voting songs. If we didn't know the words all we had to do was look at the pictures of a man then we would know who to sing for! And who to vote for! So we sang and we sang till our lungs felt as though they'd burst. And I wondered to myself, why didn't they have voting days every week. Or even every day because everyone was so happy and so nice to one another. Many of us thought of writing to the king to have more voting days because voting days were happy days . . . "For when I was a child." . . .

But we didn't get all those things that the posters and the leaflets said that we would get. Because after all the colours and the lorries and the men had all gone we were still in our old house without a garden two stairs up. And we didn't get any more to eat. I didn't anyway because I asked my mother for money for sweets one day and she told me she couldn't give me any because she couldn't afford it. Then I told her what the men with the flowers in their buttonholes had said to me. And she told me they were just telling lies. My mother also said that some of the things that were on those leaflets weren't all true . . .

" Being a child I spoke as a child . . ." I was very sad that people were telling me so many lies and I told my mother that I would pray for those people who told lies. She said that would be good. She also said that if I prayed hard enough perhaps they might not tell any more lies ever. So I prayed very hard to God not to punish them too much and not to send them to "The Bad Fire".

However as I began to grow older I was soon to find out that prayers alone weren't enough to stop lies being told about you or indeed on your behalf. Boys who sat next to you in class at school could also tell lies about you. Like telling the teacher you weren't listening when you were listening. And as a boy I tried to be as tough as they were. But I knew that deep down I wasn't. But I also knew that I was better at football than most of them. Because I could dribble the ball past most of them in the playground at play-time. And they didn't like that. Perhaps that was why they told the teacher lies about me.

I didn't like school because there was a lot of fighting at school and I didn't like fighting. Maybe it was because I was smaller and always came off worst if there was a fight. But I didn't tell anyone about it. Not even my mother when I got home. Because I knew she would only tell me to keep away from them. But I did like sitting on my roll in the classroom to keep it nice and warm for playtime so that I could eat it and lick the margarine from my roll as it oozed out of the sides.

The shop at our corner sold the best rolls in the world I bet. I could eat two or three at a time but I was only allowed to take one to school with me because my mother said I had to think of my other brothers and sisters who were much older than me and had bigger appetites. And that she could only afford to buy a certain amount. For I was a child and believed her. She also said that the others were working and therefore needed more. But often she gave me the thick outside slice of an ordinary loaf and sometimes that tasted almost as good as a roll when it was toasted.

I also loved Fridays when my mother bought fish for all of us for our supper, and fat succulent chips to go with the fish. We also got plenty of bread and margarine just in case we didn't have enough chips. The fish my mother used to get was called ling. And it came in squares all tied up with string. I used to watch my mother take off the string the night before and soak the fish in water overnight. It was very salty and made all of us drink a lot of water afterwards. But I didn't mind because I liked drinking water. Sometimes my mother would slip me a few more chips because she said I was the baby of the family.

My mother cooked the chips in fresh beef dripping which she bought from the butcher's shop on the corner because she said he was the best butcher in the whole of Glasgow. And I believed her. Because my mother never told me any lies when I was little. But my big brothers did and sometimes they would tell me not to tell my mother that I had seen them talking to girls.

But sometimes I told my mother that I had seen them talking to girls and they would be angry with me. And said I should be ashamed of myself. "When I was a child I spoke as a child . . . "They also said that I would be the same age as they were in about twelve years time and I would be in the same boat as them. But I told them that I didn't want to go in a boat with them or anyone else.

And I didn't care. Because my mother had told me that it was a sin to tell a lie . Big brothers were sometimes worse than big sisters. Big sisters sometimes told lies too, but not as many as those voting people. Big sisters were always giggling together, and when you asked them what they were laughing at they would say that they were laughing at nothing. But you can't laugh at nothing. It's got to be at something. Because that's what my teacher said. And teachers are always right our headmaster said. "When I was a child . . ."

My mother was very clever because she could make emulsion. And that was one of the times I didn't want her to be clever because I didn't like emulsion. None of us did. My mother used to get condensed milk which I liked, then she would spoil it all by mixing it with stuff called malt. She would then stir it all together and give it to us in large spoonfuls. It was awful but she made us take it twice a day. My mother said it would stop us all getting plukes and styes in our eyes and spots on our faces..

But the very next week I had two spots on my face and they didn't go away. I told mother about it but she said that didn't matter and that I still had to take my emulsion. Maybe my mother was telling lies now too. So I asked her if she was telling lies and she said no she wasn't telling lies. Then I asked her why I was getting all those spots when emulsion was supposed to stop them coming on my face. She then said that the emulsion didn't stop the spots. It only helped to stop the spots.

And she told me that she wasn't telling lies if she said that the emulsion only helped to stop the spots. I then asked her if it would help me stop getting styes altogether. The next day and every day after that my mother stopped giving me emulsion . . . "When I was a child I thought as a child . . ." My mother used to comb my hair often with a very fine toothed comb. Because she said I was the youngest of the family and it got rid of all the bogeymen from my scalp. She also used to wash me with soap called Berback. And I didn't like that either. She made me stand in our little sink which she called a Jawbox. And she would wash me down with this Berback soap which I didn't like. I asked my mother why the little sink in the kitchen was called a Jawbox and why she didn't just wash my jaw if it was called that. But she didn't answer me. Maybe she was too tired.

Then she would make me kneel down with my head on her lap and she would use the fine comb. She would put a newspaper on her lap. She said it was to see when the bogeymen fell out of my head. When they did fall out she would squeeze them on the back of the comb and there would be a loud bang. Sometimes I could see the bogeymen lying dead on the newspaper and sometimes there would be blood from them.

It wasn't very nice. But still my mother kept looking for more. I thought that was very cruel. So I said to my mother was that not a sin to kill little beasties like that. But she said no that it was not a sin to kill little beasties like that. Yes she knew that they were God's beasties. But that there were too many of them and that they would have died anyway. Then she said she would be very glad when I grew up and became a man. And I thought that was very nice of my mother to say that . . . "When I became a man, I thought as a man. And I put away the things of a child . . ."

And grow up, I did. I was the only one still at school when my father announced that we would all be moving to a much larger house away up in Carntyne which was miles away. But we would have a front and back garden and a bathroom with a real bath in it. It really was a very nice place to be staying in was Carntyne. The streets were a lot quieter and there was lots of greenery and wide open spaces where you could play football. There would be no need to play football in the street and that meant you couldn't get into trouble for breaking a shop window or something like that.

I liked playing football because I was good at it. And I wasn't good at many things. But I was good at football and singing. I liked singing a lot and often sang to myself when just walking along the road. Sometimes that was the best way to learn a song. Because you had plenty of peace time to sing the words and make them nice and clear. And better still there was no one there to criticise you even if you were rotten. But I didn't think I was rotten too often. It was difficult to tell. Some people said I was good and sounded like Bing Crosby. But some others said I was rotten and sounded nothing like him. Anyway they could say and think what they liked. It.wouldn't stop me singing.

The only thing I missed when my family moved to Carntyne were my pals. I missed them quite a lot. I hadn't many but the few I had were loyal and like myself hadn't left school yet. But I was beginning to take notice of things apart from football and singing. I was beginning to take note of my new surroundings. I knew I could sing as long as I liked by myself but I couldn't play football by myself. And as my brothers were too old to play football there was no one around for me to play football with. Perhaps I would have to look for others to play with. I didn't know any other boys around because they were also new to Carntyne having just moved there. Because it was a brand new housing estate just built to help families like my own, new faces were arriving every day. And I also knew that I would have to meet some of them some day.

Some boys had no difficulty in asking other boys if they could join in a game at football or any other game. But I couldn't. I tried one day but drew back at the last minute. At night sometimes especially when the days grew longer, I would hear a ball being punted about somewhere. And I was sorely tempted to go outside and try and find the place and perhaps pluck up enough courage to ask them for a game, because footballs were very scarce and very costly. Real footballs with an inside bladder, I mean. My parents could never have afforded to buy one never in a million years. My next oldest brother Charlie was only two years older than me, but he didn't like football and anyway he was always working in a pub. So I asked my mother if it would be alright if I went back to the Calton where I used to stay to play football and she said yes. But that it was good distance away. Almost three whole miles.

She also said she was very sorry that she couldn't afford to give me money for the tram and the bus to get there. I told her that was OK and that I was young and strong enough to walk there and back . She said. "We'll see." So I tried it after school one day and it took me over an hour to get there. So when I was finished playing football with my old pals I didn't walk back. I ran back and it only took me half an hour. It was great. Because I loved playing football and if I practised long enough and hard enough perhaps Celtic might spot me and sign me. But I always had to run back because if I didn't I wouldn't have been able to get home before dark. And my father said that nine o'clock was the deadline in the summer.

So I played football, walked and ran back two or three times a week after school; even more when we were on school holidays. I didn't mind, because sometimes I would get a lift in a lorry from a lorry driver who said he had spotted me every so often running along Gallowgate and down Abercromby street. He wouldn't believe me at first when I told him where I was running from and where I was running back to. "That's almost three miles," he said. "Do you realize that?" I said I did but that I didn't mind. "You should become a Harrier," he said. "You could become a world champion if you put your mind to it." But I told him that I would rather be a footballer and maybe play for Celtic some day or be a Singer like Bing Crosby. "Well," he said, "if you become either of those things you'll not be needing me to keep giving you lifts all the time. Will you?"

He was a very nice man and as good as his word. Any time he saw me on the road after that he would stop and give me a lift. I did that round trip for almost a year then I sat down one day and told myself that I would have to grow up even faster if I was to survive. Then my mother took a hand in the proceedings. "you'll soon be leaving school, Teddy," she said. "I know," I replied. "Well," she said. "You'll just have to find new friends then won't you?" And I agreed.

"Then, why don't you go over to that place they call the Riddrie Knowes. It's just round the corner as I'm sure you're aware. Just go round some day and see who they all are and ask then if you can have a game? They won't bite you know. And just think of all the time and energy you'll save by not having to run down to the Calton every other day. "My mother was right as usual. It's something I should have thought of a long time ago. Because even most of the pals I was running down to Glasgow's East End to play with were also moving away too.

It had something to do with "Slum Clearance" someone told me. So I decided to take the bull by the horns and went round one night during the Easter holidays to see this Riddrie Knowes everyone was talking about. And it was all that the local papers had said it was, in an editorial they had done as a welcoming gesture to new incomers. Although there was a row of houses away up high to the right, The Knowes was a lovely little green valley a sort of rural knoll that had survived all the new building works that had been going on all around for a very long time. The valley itself was roughly oval shaped and ideal for football cricket and any other kind of game you could care to mention.

Not only that, but as if to make present day youngsters think of the past there was another added attraction. High up and well away from the playing surface there was a lovely ridge of huge rocks; real rocks; hewn out of walled stone reminiscent of decades gone by. And tailor- made for anyone wanting to sledge or to toboggan. Which indeed it was used for I was later to learn every snowy Christmas that God sent. All this had been literally next door to me without my realizing it. And just a couple of miles away from Glasgow's bustling city centre. It was a Paradise in the fullest sense of the word.

It took me ages to really take it all in. Finally someone shouted over to me. "Want a game?" I didn't know what to say. But I did manage to give a vigorous nod of assent . . . "OK then. Get your jacket off and let's see what you can do." I was in. At least I thought I was in. But I would have to prove myself. So as soon as I got the ball I trapped it with my right foot until the tackle came in then I weaved and turned as I knew I could and headed for the goal. We played for about half an hour, and I was made most welcome. I was asked where I came from. What school I was at. What team did I support. So I told them. It was at that moment I got the impression that I wouldn't have to look for a game any more. They would be looking for me. And it was a comforting thought.

It was the beginning of a new life for me. New pals playing the game I loved and who somehow liked the way I played it. I played all through the Easter holidays and most of the summer. And surprisingly I was introduced to the game of cricket for the very first time. Before I'd always thought that cricket was a "cissy" game. A kind of adult "rounders" but with a hard ball. I was pleasantly surprised to find out that it was far from that. It was then I saw for the very first time what a real cricket bat looked and felt like. I was amazed at the weight of it too. Made out of the willow tree I was told.

At first I thought it would impossible to hold let alone wield to connect with a real life cricket ball. Sadly not for me I thought since I wasn't exactly the biggest or strongest boy in the world for my age. But I was proved wrong. I took to the game. And acquitted myself reasonably well I was told. It was also the first baptism I'd ever had with real cricket pads. One of the boys it so happened, who'd been playing football with us owned the whole set. A cricket bat with real springs in it, balls, pads and wickets. In fact the whole caboodle as they used to say then. His parents had bought him the set for his Christmas I was told.

And I remembered thinking at the time that his father must have been very rich. He most certainly was a par above being a labourer with Glasgow Corporation's Water Department like my own father. Not that I loved my father any less mind you for that. But it made you think just the same. It made me think anyway. I later found out that this lad's name was Steel, Johnnie Steel and you would never have dreamed he was from a rich family. His father, seemingly was a director of some large firm. But it was to Johnnie Steel that I owed my gratitude. For it was he who taught me how to hold a bat and face a bowler and even how to deal with googlies which to a boy my size was a very daunting task.

Johnnie himself was no mean footballer either not unlike my own style of play. Perhaps that was why we got on so well. And if he's still around today I hope he reads this. For it was he who gave me an insight into the game of cricket. And showed me that it just wasn't a game for the elite English people. Because Johnnie Steel was as Scottish as I was and just as good at football as I was. And for the whole of my last summer holidays from school we played football then cricket till we could play no more. Then we would lie down to cool down with a bottle of pop.

Those days when I had just turned fourteen I felt were some of the happiest days of my life. I remembered Johnnie Steel saying his goodbyes to us all one day later in the summer. His family were moving away to England. Something to do with his father's business he told me. Curiously enough although I was one of the last to join the gang who played football and cricket in Riddrie Knowes somehow I became his confidante. It was he who pulled me aside one day and told that he had been asked to play a trial for an English club who were then in the English Second Division. He then asked me not to tell the rest of the gang.

I wondered why at the time. Maybe he thought we would all think he was blowing his own horn. But why tell me? The more I thought about it, the more puzzled I became. Then it struck me. Our styles were similar although he was much bigger. Perhaps what he was trying to give me was hope. The more I thought about it the more convinced I became. What he was trying to say to me was that if he could make it, I could make it too. And that I might follow in his footsteps and get a trial for my own favourite football team Celtic. No such luck there however.

But I've often since wondered if that's what he was trying to say to me that day. Then I lost track. Because when you're only fourteen and about to leave school and have a father breathing down your neck to get a job; any job, you don't get round to reading many newspapers. But anyway Johnnie Steel wherever you are I hope you made it with Barnsley at football. And if not, with an English county side at cricket. But for me a job I most certainly would have to get if I was to pay my way at home. Playing football and cricket were all very well my father would say but it didn't pay the rent unless you were a professional and could earn lots of money for doing it. Which was something I couldn't do.

A very old proverb was put in reverse as far as I was concerned. "All play and no work can make Jack a very unpopular boy". Which I was, where my father was concerned. Work was the most important thing in his life as well as trade unionism. Everything else was of secondary importance. Even my mother had to remonstrate with him sometimes on his almost tyrannical views on the subject. I did however manage to get a job even if it was just for a week-end. It was with the local grocers. I was provided with a bicycle with a basket on front of the handlebars. My job was to deliver groceries to housebound people and perhaps even lazy people who couldn't be bothered to go round to the shop and get their own groceries. At least, that's how I saw it.

And for the short time I was there I really enjoyed it. First of all it was very pleasant driving around on a bicycle. Because my parents couldn't afford to buy me one of my own. That in itself was an achievement as far as I was concerned. And sometimes I made as much two shillings in tips in one morning. And as you no doubt guessed most of the tips came from old people who I felt could ill afford to hand out money they just did not have. Predictably there very few tips if any from those well-heeled customers who just wanted their groceries delivered free of charge in more ways than one. And that made me very angry.

But like all good things my delivery job didn't last. It all fell apart one Saturday morning. Scotland were playing England. It was to be on the radio and the Great Raymond Glendinning was to be giving the commentary. And I wanted so desperately to hear it. All those things were on my mind as I hurriedly pushed my bicycle into the shop.

What followed was disastrous. Boxes of fruit were on display outside the front of the shop unfortunately for me and they just happened to be apples and oranges. And boy, did those apples and oranges roll? I'll say they did. In my haste to get my deliveries finished and to get back to hear the game on the radio I accidentally rammed my bike against those boxes which were positioned adroitly but precariously outside the shop.

I could only stand aghast as apples and oranges rolled off the boxes, off the pavement, then on to the road. It was though they were racing each other to see which one of them could get to the corner first. I tried in vain to limit the damage by haring after them and picking them up from the ground. And I did actually manage to get some of them back on their perches by dint of sheer hard work. But alas it was no longer a case of apples and oranges. It was simply a case of too little too late as far as my job was concerned. News of the disaster had reached the manager in the back shop.

The manager was livid. I tried to explain, and told him that I was even prepared to forego my session by the radio complete with Raymond Glendinning and all to try and undo any damage I may have caused. But he was having none of it. "You young people of today have no respect for persons or their possessions. Just go and get your jacket. You are sacked as from this very moment!" he shouted pompously. I knew then that I was fighting a losing battle. And I well may have murmured something under my breath. "What was that you said?" he snarled. But again I bit my lip and said nothing. Suddenly everything was beginning to fall apart for me.

I went in to the shop, came out with my jacket on and was handed an envelope containing my wages. Inside the envelope was the princely sum of seven shillings and sixpence. It should have been eight shillings. I was just about to go the front shop and tell him so in front of all the customers when I noticed a little note inside. It read: "Wages- Eight Shillings,- Less Sixpence For Damaged Fruit." I was in two minds what to do. Then decided that discretion was the better part of valour. My mother would have agreed. So I walked out of the shop with just my seven and sixpence. But with my head held high.

I salvaged some solace by listening to the game on the radio. And in a way I was glad I was free to listen to it. Because it was to be a Red Letter Day in the annals of broadcasting, the newspapers said. For the first time ever listeners would be able to tell exactly where the ball was on the park even as the commentator spoke. Each newspaper showed a chart of a football field split up into about eight squares. Which meant that when Raymond Glendinning or whoever was doing the commentary said. "The ball has gone out of play," another voice would interject immediately and say "Square two." The listener would then go immediately to his chart and plot the spot where the play would be. It was almost as good as being there. An ingenious plan I thought. It was history in the making. Another giant step in the annals of broadcasting!

That day was most certainly historical in more ways than one. But there was a price that had to be paid. My father had to be told. And it fell to my mother to do just that. The surprising thing was that he didn't take it all that badly. "These are all dead end jobs son," he said. "It's maybe just as well you got the sack. You don't want to be a messenger boy all your life. Do you?" I shook my head. "Next week I suggest you take yourself down to some of the big engineering shops and see what you can get there." I was tempted to tell him that I didn't want to be an engineer all my life either. But I was learning from my mother exactly when and how to keep quiet, especially where my father was concerned.

So I did just that. After the game there was a news bulletin. And despite my somewhat depressed state, I listened intently. The bulletin was terse and to the point. "It has just been announced, that the British High Commissioner in Berlin has had further talks with Herr Hitler this morning. And our man in Berlin who had a meeting with our minister later stated that he was quietly confident that the German Chancellor had no immediate plans to march on Poland or any other European country for the foreseeable future . . ."

## Chapter Twelve

*A Land Fit For Heroes Not Seeking Pensions*

If the Germans had only known in 1939 that the Great British Army could only afford one soldier's uniform between two of us I often shudder to think what might have happened. But obviously they didn't know, otherwise they would have been across that channel quicker than you could say "Operation Overlord". And would indeed have given a whole new meaning to the phrase "Two for The Price of One" prisoner-of-war wise that is had they but acted promptly enough and managed to make it over here. But they didn't did they?

Still it was nevertheless true. Whether it was a propaganda stunt dreamed up by MI5 to snare the Huns into thinking that all our soldiers were six feet tall or over, I'll never know but somehow I doubt it. The simple fact was that we just didn't have enough uniforms to go round, round the right people that is. For those that did go round didn't go round so to speak.

For unless you wear a stock size all you got was half a battle-dress. If you were under five feet six or so you could not be fitted with a complete battle-dress at least not for some considerable time. So imagine if you can Glasgow albeit No Mean City was not exactly famous for producing giants mean or otherwise. And those citizens mean height averaged only five feet five. Put all those things together and you had a big tailoring problem. So we had to stick together in more ways than one. Because uniforms could not be found to fit short–arses like us.

Talk about "Wha's like us..?" "Damn Few" had to be the answer to that one for rhetorically speaking we just couldn't be fitted out by the English, of all people. If the blouse fitted the trousers didn't. If the trousers fitted which was seldom the blouse didn't. And conversely or perversely which ever way you looked at it if the trousers fitted that's how it was way back in December 1939 in Gosport, just beside Portsmouth. If the Bosche had only been watching us through their binoculars as we had been told they could well be things might have been different today. If only they had watched and paid attention, who knows German may well have been our second language. Maybe even our first. Ha ha . . .

That was the set up then. Since most battle-dresses had to be altered to fit and were in the hands of tailors (Somewhere in England. All very hush-hush you know) we had to move around in groups. One "fully" dressed soldier would have a "chitty" which read something along the lines of "Please excuse the following servicemen for not being properly dressed. This is due to alterations being made to uniforms to fit." All this in case we were apprehended by your friend and my friend those jolly old Redcaps as we tried to mind our own business and walk around the city.

The critical times came when the call of nature beckoned and some of us needed the toilet. Just wanting to do it in private however was not possible. That most certainly did not warrant a senior soldier with a chitty in his hand standing outside a public convenience just to suit one particular soldier's needs. We were urged therefore to go in pairs at least to save time. And to force ourselves if necessary to do without going at all, or even to wet ourselves and be proud so to do for the sake of The War Effort if for no other reason.

And only one of three of us had an army coat. That was another but very exclusive luxury. It was a great pity that those topcoats didn't fit we short-arses as well as those long-arses. For like I said it was December. And this was Portsmouth. And already almost half of His Majesty's Army were walking about only half dressed. Not particularly funny at the time for some soldiers maybe. But very amusing on looking back.

One particular time springs to mind. It was shortly after I had been called up and there was an attempt by the army to make a driver out of me. I was chosen to go on a driving course with a view to making me capable of taking over one of their many 30 cwt Bedfords. After about two weeks I was deemed to have passed my test. The test was simple, too simple for my liking; the training I thought hadn't been long enough. All it consisted of was myself at the wheel driving around town for about ten minutes with a registered driver sitting beside me shouting instructions. If you didn't knock anyone down in that ten minutes. That was it. You had passed. You were a driver.

It should be stressed that you could even bruise a few civilians on the way and still get away with it which I may well unconsciously have done but I got through. Because it was 1940 and there were too many Bedford trucks and not enough drivers to drive them, so I guess I had to pass. Ready or not sort of thing like a game of hide and seek I thought. But being of a nervous disposition I didn't feel comfortable when driving a Bedford or any other motor vehicle for that matter. I tried to tell the Transport Section this but was told to shut up and get on with it.

This I did. However the next thing was that only days after having just passed my driving test I was made duty driver for a week to see how I got on. It also came to pass that being duty driver meant one of the tasks entrusted to you was to transport the sick parade to the nearest town to see the medical officer. You and your vehicle then had to wait until the sick had been attended to. That done you then had to transport them all the way back to camp again. It was all good selfless biblical stuff, looking after the sick And I was glad to be the chosen one.

So with the best will in the world I presented myself and my Bedford truck to the camp gate to to await the sick parade and to take them to town to be administered to.

It goes without saying too that another task that fell to the Duty Driver was to help aboard the truck those unable to make it by themselves such as those with broken ankles, blistered feet and the odd dislocated shoulders not to mention those suffering from with or to give them their good old Glasgow rhyming slang name, "The Duke Of Argylls." All this I may say I did without demur. Then when all were aboard I would set off for town. And my mission? "To Help The Blind To See.".and "The Lame To Walk.".like the Good Book says. But in all fairness I thought the least that the Good Lord could have done would to have afforded me better road conditions that morning on my first foray into the unknown . . . .

The roads were icy so I decided to cut my speed considerably and negotiated the five miles or so into town with reasonable consistency and steady speed and even braking, with concentration. I was doing all those things the instructor had told me to do albeit somewhat hurriedly. I even had time to shout back to my passengers in the back like all good drivers should. "Everyone okaydokay back there?" The response I got from the back however I felt was somewhat less than enthusiastic. But no matter, I was down to about twenty five miles an hour and was giving my instructor's ego a tremendous boost. He would have been proud of me I thought, if he could but see me. Then it happened. Inexplicably, but it happened. And those stricken passengers in the back would testify to that to this very day . . .

I had reached the top of a hill that then sloped down into the small town when I spotted an open-topped double -decker bus ahead. It was thronged with civilians going to work. Some on top. Some below deck. It was about five hundred yards ahead of me. All the time in the world to brake, I thought. But it would be a gentle type of braking like the instructor had warned, so I strove to keep cool and applied my brakes gently but firmly still well away from that bus some two hundred yards ahead.

The bus then pulled up at a bus stop at the bottom of the hill. I could even see some passengers ready to alight on to the pavement and others coming down the upstairs deck seemed to be waving to me. Nice of them I remembered thinking to myself, no doubt pleased to know their army's presence was at hand to protect them, a kind of safety valve if you like. It was then I noticed that the waving was becoming more frantic and erratic. I also happened to notice that my speed had increased without my knowing it and I was skidding quickly, very quickly indeed into the back of that bus.

I had committed the unforgivable sin of not combining the use of my clutch together with my brakes as I'd been instructed to do and this had forced my truck to skid bang into the back of that bus. To make matters even worse my truck had unfortunately hit the middle of the stairs on that double-decker making it impossible for those upstairs to get down from the top deck. Some had to resort to sliding down the outside rail clutching their briefcases as they went in an effort to reach the bottom deck. And they were very angry. Especially one old lady who kept hitting me over the head repeatedly with her umbrella after I'd got out to see the damage. "See what you've done you silly soldier" she screamed and shouted. "Now I can't get to my work." Others too were shaking their fists at me. The driver was a bit more civilized and accepted my apology when I admitted it was my fault. Fortunately no one was seriously hurt.

But there was worse to come. I'd momentarily forgotten that I too had passengers in the back of my truck. So I went round to see how they were and got lots of moans from those inside. "How are we going to get into town now to see the M.O.?" one of them screamed. But I had no answer to that. The whole front bonnet had caved in. Fortunately we were only about a quarter of a mile from the doctor's premises. I tried unsuccessfully to get help from passing traffic. And as I was required by law to stay with my vehicle, all I could do was to apologize to them again. and at the same time lay it on the line. But as far as they were concerned, it was a case of "Take Up Thy Bed And Walk." Which they eventually but reluctantly did cursing me as they limped, hobbled and shuffled their weary bodies into town . . .

I was put on a charge when I got back." Seven days Confined for Careless Driving." That's what they gave me. I then asked the Transport Sergeant to be relieved from my driving duties. But I was told I couldn't. "We're short of drivers." I was told in no uncertain terms. They must have been, I thought, if they still wanted me. But I had gone off the whole notion of driving. The mere thought of sitting behind a wheel again filled me with despair. Indeed so short of drivers were they that the very next week I was put on a night driving exercise . . .

Night driving meant driving without any lights whatsoever. It consisted solely of stopping and starting, stopping and starting again all through the night in convoy along narrow unlit track roads. The whole thing was a nightmare. Trying desperately not to doze off and ram the truck in front of you was another very live hazard. To make matters even worse they had loaded all the platoon's rations on to my truck. That meant if I didn't make it, the rest didn't eat for the next three days. Now there was strategic planning for you . . . I had just discovered too that not only could I not drive in daylight with all lights blazing, but predictably I couldn't drive at night either with no lights at all blazing . . .

All the jerking forward and the abrupt halts and jolts, and the stalling of the engine finally took it's toll and I finished up in a ditch with my truck lying at an angle of forty five degrees with myself and my co-driver immersed in muck up to our ears. We would be there all night we were told until the crane came and yanked us out of the ditch the following morning. Those platoon members in the back came off even worse having to spend most of the night trying to tease sugar, jam and condensed milk out of their hair. When morning did break, I was dismayed to hear that further up the track other starving members of that same platoon were shouting for my head on the proverbial platter. Maybe now I thought I would be relieved of "my command".

But believe it or not I wasn't. The officer in charge of the whole operation had decreed that all drivers who had finished up in ditches were to be exonerated due to the bad road conditions at the time. So I was still officially a driver as far as the army was concerned. I just couldn't see myself getting out of it, unless of course I ran over the C.O. Even then I suppose to make doubly sure I would have required to reverse and go back over him again at twice the speed before I could get away from driving. I felt as though I would never get off it. That should give anyone an idea just how short the army was of drivers at that particular time.

Duty called once more in the form of another exercise. This time "Exercise Bravo." Although I had another name for it. This particular exercise was meant to emphasize to us the importance of continuity convoy cohesion. This seemingly meant that a certain distance would be required to be kept between each vehicle and that speeds would vary as dictated. But by whom I wondered. I was to find out very soon. We were to proceed in convoy to a fixed destination at speeds controlled by despatch riders who would be in charge of those speeds. They and they alone would convey to us by various signals when to increase and when to decrease those speeds. All trucks would be loaded up as they would be in action. That is, four squaddies in the back, a driver and a Lance Jack in front. And so it was. I thought I had handled the first ten miles or so very well as did the newly made up Lance Jack beside me. I even thought I detected singing coming from the back of my truck.

Dunkirk had been evacuated only weeks before and the Top Brass were determined to erase it from our memories. And no, there was absolutely no truth in the rumour that Churchill wanted all reverse gears taken out of all British vehicles. We were to think positively. And be realistic. And anyone discussing our defeat at "you know where" would be for the high jump and no mistake. So we were back to the Olympics again were we? Magnificent in defeat and all that guff. It was all second prize stuff once more just like my old team Celtic again who when I last heard were now claiming that corner kicks should be counted as goals . . .

I took a corner a little too sharply and just managed to right it at the last minute with a despatch rider sitting on his bike at the corner waving a reproving finger at me as I passed. They all had cards which they held up carrying messages like "Reduce Speed" and "Increase Speed". Some had even more ominous ones like " You are one point five seconds behind vehicle in front. Increase speed now." Those sort of signs I did not like. Nor did that innocent looking young Lance Jack sitting beside me either methinks.

I thought I detected a squirm from him as I stepped up the speed to obey that last command from the man on the bike. I could hear movement and the shuffling of bodies in the back. The singing had stopped. Things were becoming much more serious now. So I decided to give it all my attention. Third time lucky as they say, or someone was supposed to have said. But it did not happen. Another signal to give it the boot was flashed to me which I immediately strove to respond to and in so doing succeeded in over-locking my steering a little too much and struck a kerb. At least I hoped it was a kerb. My truck then swerved out of control. I tried desperately to recover control again. But it was to no avail. I appeared to be hitting one side of the road then screwing across to the other side with monotonous regularity.

Khaki clad bodies were also being unloaded at regular intervals on to the road. Were they from my vehicle I wondered? It was just as well for me that I was only managing about twenty miles per hour at the time. I dreaded to think what would have happened had I obeyed that last D.R.s signal to the letter. Again fortunately for me no one was seriously hurt. But bruises in abundance were reported.

This time I hoped and prayed that I would be taken off driving for good. And I was. But only after I was asked the reason for my losing control. I explained what I had done. And how I had fought to gain control again. And once more my explanation was accepted. They would send me on one more driving course to improve my efficiency if I wished. But I declined and backed up by my medical officer I won my point.

I asked for a transfer from the Army School of Driving and was successful. I was transferred to another company. A company still within the battalion. And that company was "The Argyll and Sutherland Highlanders"( Machine Gun Section ) where I was to finally find my niche as a rangetaker with the famous "Barr & Stroud Rangefinder." So as far as I was concerned it was a case of Exit "The World's Worst Driver" and Enter "The World's Best Rangetaker". I hoped.

These were to be revolutionary times for The Vickers 303 from The Great War. For they were now to be mounted on converted Bren Carriers which would enhance even more their undoubted war winning potential. For this bunch of soldiers I considered to be as near to my heart as those I had as passengers when driving were to my throat. And it would be with these men that I would train. And it would be with these men that I would go into battle.

"What's on this morning?" This would often be the call to the few who always made it down from our Nissen hut to the dining hall for breakfast. And more often than not the reply would invariably be the same. "Rissoles!" . . . It was then the sighs would commence and the toasting of illicit bread would ensue. Most bunks would have long lengths of wire with slices of bread stuck on the end that could reach the top stove from any distance. Even from the entry door. And all because "arseholes" weren't the most popular of breakfasts being only marginally above kippers and haricot beans for The Table D'hote. But occasionally, Just occasionally, surprises would surface when that question would be answered by an already satisfied customer. "They've got eggs on but you'd better be quick. There's not many left." The Nissen hut would then empty as the scampering would begin to get suitably dressed to get down to greet those eggs down in the dining hall.

Food took on an enormous significance if only for the lack of it. Yet it was surprising just how much food was actually wasted in the army either through ignorance or due simply to bad organization or even poorer distribution. And boredom was a constant threat to discipline. Finding the troops something constructive to do was becoming more and more difficult. And there was a limit to how many exercises and route marches that men could be put through. Inactivity was even more prevalent around 1942 when nothing was happening on the War Front.

Or anywhere else for that matter. A certain nothingness permeated everywhere. Stagnation was about to take over the British Army lock, stock and barrel. That was when the slogan *"If It Does Not Move Paint It"* was really activated. And if anyone was ever around an army camp somewhere in Britain round about that time must have noticed that every conceivable piece of structure be it railings, posts or boxes were all painted white. Mostly because that was the only colour that was around. It became a fetish. And soon every camp in the country was at the painting game whether that object needed painting or not.

Cleanliness had suddenly taken over from Hitler. And it had nothing at all to do with godliness either. Enter then the indefatigable brigadier obviously bored out of his skull too like the rest of us otherwise nothing would ever have taken root. Nor would he have ever embarked on that fact-finding mission with regards to food and it's uses, not to mention it's mis-uses. But as before there were hidden agendas in those instances when such an inspection was on. Look-outs were posted illegally . And when the Brig. and his entourage were spotted coming along the road the look-outs would dutifully signal back to the camp. The camp would then be put on full alert. Everything would then be ready, highly polished and freshly painted for the "Great Advent".

But these said camps were not to know about this fact-finding mission the brigadier was bent on. They do say however that on one occassion the Top Brass's convoy swept through one of those magnificent white gates with a flourish in the early morning sunlight. And that the brigadier alighted briskly from his "chariot" to copy-book salutes from officers and men alike. Not only that but almost the whole of the Army Catering Corps were also represented there in their spotlessly white uniforms.

And they stood there erect at the salute to a man it is said. Then not according to plan, the brigadier, they do say, asked to be taken to the rear of the cookhouse. His wish was granted immediately. Whereupon it is also said he divested himself of his tunic and stick, handed them to his aide, rolled up his sleeve to the elbow, plunged his arm straight down into the bowels of one of the many swill tubs that stood there and withdrew a whole loaf of bread and held it aloft triumphantly.

He then repeated the action and came up with another loaf of bread much to the consternation of the still standing, still saluting, members of the Army Catering Corps. Not to mention an equally aggrieved company commander standing there open-mouthed. The story goes that the brigadier put the officer in charge of the Royal Army Catering Corps on a charge for wasting food . . . And the commanding officer copped it too they say for allowing such waste to take place on a camp under his command.

Those were the sort of things that came leaping out at you when looking back. Not those bad times. Most certainly not the fear. But the fun things. For they must always overshadow the bad things. I have no regrets. Like when my mother wrote to me when I had only been in the army a short while. Could I go and see if my big brother Tam was alright? After all he was only about twelve years older than I was and he hadn't been in the army all that long having volunteered shortly after I was called up.

As far as my mother knew Tam was just down the road somewhere in Wiltshire. I was stationed in Kent. As was to be expected my mother's geographic knowledge of England wasn't all that good. It was tantamount to saying . "I know you're in America Teddy. But your brother's just up the road from you in Canada. I wonder if you would just go up and see if he's alright . . ."

So I heeded my mother's plea and went to see Tam like a good young brother should. I had to thumb lift after lift to get there in various army vehicles. I actually finished the last five miles inside a Sherman tank. But I finally got there after about five hours on the road. It took me another hour to find the forest where The Royal Army Service Corps were billeted.

It was a forest dense with trees and rows and rows of army trucks lining a field parallel to the woods. And behind the vehicles more rows and rows of Nissen huts.

I hadn't been all that many Christmases in the army myself as far as I can remember. And I shall never forget it for all the wrong reasons. The very first hut I came to had a large message painted on the front door. And it read;

"Christmas Comes But Once A Year.
Corporal McCann Drinks All The Beer."

That was my big brother alright. So I had a few drinks with my brother, acting Sergeant Corporal McCann. To be fair he did organize some transport to get me back to camp to beat the reveille deadline. But unfortunately the truck broke down and I had to walk the last five miles or so back to my own camp. I didn't beat that deadline. Got five days confined. But wrote my mother a letter the very next morning. "Dear Mother. Went and seen Tam. He's fine."

The army was still trying desperately to combat that old friend, boredom. Farming was the next thing to come to the rescue round about that time. A lot of farmers had been called up leaving them very short of man-power. And so as with many others, our platoon was farmed out to do just that in Scotland. We farmed. We stooked barley. We made hay. We even took on that most back-breaking task of all. "Tattie Howking." Now anyone who has ever done any howking will tell you that it is one of the most soul destroying jobs ever. And no one would argue with that. Let me tell you!

Each one of us was given a twenty yard stretch of ground to howk. And howk it, you'd better had. At first we all thought it would be a piece of cake. How wrong! Along would come a tractor propelling spuds up out of the ground. Catch them if you can, and stick them into the buckets provided. Easie peasie we reckoned, and we were soon at the ready with hands and pails awaiting that old tractor to do it's worst as it came round again, again, and again. When we missed a few, and we did miss a few lot of times, we would try and tramp them into the ground again when we thought no one was looking.

And anyway we thought that the tractor was bound to stop cascading those spuds into the air sometime. But it didn't. Not ever. No sooner had you cleared your drill and were taking a breather than it was on top of you again, again and again. Some of us resorted to sabotage to try to get that infernal machine to stop. But it never worked. We even tried jamming the wheels with stones as it passed when we thought no one was looking. Often we tried hefty kicks at the wheels but without success. That tractor was virtually indestructible and unstoppable.

And on and on it would go. Potatoes virtually rained down on us. One squaddie in tears began to curse aloud. "I thought the R.S.P.A. meant a society for the prevention of cruelty to animals. But what's wanted here is a society for the prevention of cruelty to bloody squaddies!" He was carted away kicking and screaming. I stuck it for three days only because I hasten to add that the old farmer gave us an egg a night for every day we stuck the "tattie howking" just that bit longer. But much as I loved my egg I reneged after the fifth day and reported sick with a sore back as did many others. We were truly in agony. Our backs were breaking. We had a legitimate case. Did the bloody Germans have to do this sort of thing? We began to wonder. It certainly was cruelty on a massive scale. Then we had a stroke of luck.

It was holiday time and somehow they managed to get lots of school children to do the dirty work for money. To be fair most of us would have done anything for money. But "howking" wasn't one of them. The farmers later told us that it was literally child's play. Because being small the children didn't have to bend down as far and could do it more or less sitting down. Getting the army to do it was just a test case because there had been a shortage of potatoes at the time. I remember thinking angrily that if ever there happened to be a Potato Famine in my lifetime it wouldn't have bothered me a great deal.

Those were just some of the memories that I will take to my grave with me. And I'll treasure them. Because without them what would I have been? Certainly not a touch-typist. Perhaps a singer if I had taken my chances. Or had taken the advice of Jack Hylton's resident singer after my performance at Glasgow's Moss's Empire. I would never even have tried to survive on a fiver a week in the fifties and put my wife and two kids at risk just to get into show business. No. That wouldn't have been my way. And even if I had managed to make it to the very top as a singer it would all have been for nothing.

For no matter what road I went down there would have been no Smithy. There would have been no Jack Price. No Sonny. No Nothing. There would have been no more watching Smithy chasing loot and throwing himself across a room in Normandy thinking that he could beat the speed of sound and thwart those booby-traps. No more cracks about the Yanks. Those things I would have missed.

Those things I really would have missed. Oh yes . . . No doubt about that. For when I came out of the army in 1947 I had already been downgraded from A1 to B1. That in itself was an admission by the army that my health had suffered as a consequence of army service. Therefore it followed that my disability was attributable to the War Department. And that entitled me to a War Disability Pension from 1947. Yet for twenty three long years I received absolutely nothing.

Then in 1970 fate, luck, call it what you will intervened. Otherwise I would have been without a penny to this very day. Money that was rightfully mine. Oh yes. They did give me a suit when I left. Even that didn't fit. Because I wasn't six feet tall. I also received a few quid that was due me and a pat on the back. Oh yes. They also thanked me for what I'd done for king and country. And that was it.

Then round about 1948 a friend of mine who knew I had been awarded the M.M. asked me if I'd received my £10 annuity yet. He had read about it in a newspaper. But no ten quid had ever came my way. Because £10 was a lot of money. But then again it may well have been my own fault for not being able to afford to buy a paper.

I then remember writing to the War Office to have this £10 annuity confirmed and if confirmed to make my legitimate claim for it. A qualified but haughty reply came back. Yes. The writer was correct. The War Office through the goodness of their hearts were prepared to pay a one-off annuity as follows:- To The Holder of "The Victoria Cross" £20 . . . To The Holder of "The Military Medal" £10. The letter then went on to say that these monies would only be paid out if the claim was made on or before a certain date which they gave in the letter. And then followed a heavily underlined sentence."If any substantiated claim is not made before the aforesaid date then this money will referred to our "Moribound Account."

That was the War Office for you. Very quick with the medal. Very quick and very efficient about the Gazette Number of your particular award in the annals of war. Very enthusiastic in the warmth of their congratulations they added to the King's letter. But not a work about the few bob that they were owing to you. I had never ever heard of a"Moribound Account". My little Latin told me it was something to do with death. Could it have meant dying counting their money? I wondered. So what was it all about then in those dark secretive days shortly after the war? There used to be a propaganda message that was put about when I was in the army and it was; "Get to Know Your Enemy" I would now counsel any young soldier now by saying "Get To Know Your Rights In The Army" first. And then start getting to know the enemy!

I certainly didn't recall any talk-ins regarding our benefits. No welfare officer to spell out your entitlements. And most certainly not any commanding officers to see that "Fair Play" was administered. No, there was none of that. Just a few well chosen carefully prepared notes about making ones way in the new world without ruffling too many feathers.. And getting on with it. "There's a good chap . . . Off you jolly well go!" sort of thing and that was it.

The more ignorant you were about the facts the more they were prepared to do you for. That's what makes me at 81 a very angry old man as opposed to the very angry young man we used to hear so much about it in the sixties and seventies. Angry certainly because the people I had trusted had purposely diddled me out of hundreds of pounds. Money that I would well have done with when I'd needed it most. And this from the outfit that myself and thousands of others like me were prepared to lay down our lives for. I can only hope that any young aspiring soldier reads this and pays attention. Because if he doesn't he may well get this arm blown off and be told that it was an Act of God. And that the Army wasn't liable for an arm or a leg, or even a head wound . . .

But if he waited a few years and looked after his good arm as best he could, they may countenance paying him a small disablement pension. But regretfully that pension wouldn't be paid from the moment the arm was blown off. Because the Army didn't operate that way. Those pensions they would hasten to add were not retrospective. Because the phrase "Not retrospective" was still and as far as I know a euphemism used by the War Office for deception on a massive scale.

The mere fact that they didn't inform you of the entitlements at the time did not matter. All the better when there were people like myself or even worse with a condition identified as "Psycho Neurosis" (Anxiety State)". Even better when some cases who didn't even know what day of the week it was they were dealing with. "Far too many of that bloody sort, what..! Bomb-happy blighters . . ." One could envisage some well-heeled Colonel Blimp type saying, when reviewing how much all those blasted disablement pensions were costing the country. "Shell-shocked buggers. Don't deserve a pension at all. There was none of that nonsense in the Great War. Was there? Put the blighters down at dawn. Didn't we . . . ? And why not? No pussy-footing then by Gad! Trying to bleed the country dry for a few measly pounds, what what! "Oh no. It wasn't the War Office who were being mercenary. It was you! "Your Country Needs You!" But you were found wanting! You were after Money. Ugh! You Mercenary Blighter . . . !

And that's what we were I'm sure according to them. Shall I tell you how this mercenary bomb-happy blighter managed to get his War Disability Pension

In the early seventies my son Charles just happened to be having lunch with a well known lawyer one day and my name happened to come up. He mentioned to the lawyer how I had sustained this head injury in Holland in 1944. The lawyer asked me what sort of pension I was receiving for this war wound of mine. When Charles said I was receiving nothing the lawyer friend looked at him with incredulity. "You're joking?" Charles assured him that he wasn't. Whereupon his friend told me to claim immediately for what was rightfully mine. This I naturally did straight away..

Within a week or so I was awarded what I think was the minimum disability Pension which was twenty per cent. All this without then even looking at me. Now there was magnanimity for you. Yes but only because they'd been caught out. But guess what? They very much regretted that there would be no retrospective payment.The mere fact that I had gone in A1 and had been downgraded to B1 due to my being wounded in action made them liable automatically.

Because it was an admission that my wounds were attributable to enemy action. Whilst admitting liability they informed me that regretfully my pension was not retrospective. And more or less underlined that any loss of money incurred by me was of my own making for putting up with my disability. It wasn't their fault that I kept stumbling from one job to the other, and suffered from a chronic nervous condition i.e. the one they had certified me with "Psycho Neurosis. (Anxiety State).

They even told me that their generous award of twenty per cent was not to be taken as my preserve for ever. No. No. I would be liable periodically to go in front of a War Pensions Board in order that those wise men could see for themselves if this hand-out of theirs could be sustained by me. I supposed it was some sort of safeguard they reserved the right to present in case I suddenly threw off my yoke of neurotic behaviour went into politics and finished up as prime minister.

No flys on our war department. I didn't become prime minister. But ironically enough, I did produce a "Prime Suspect". And that was the War Pensions Board themselves when I was hauled up before them to defend my Bounty and their somewhat belated Largesse. To be fair, the tribunal offers you someone to state your case for you if you didn't feel equipped yourself so to do. But I resisted their gratuitous offer and decided to fight my own corner.

And with due solemnity they told me to proceed. Although I was sure I could hear a very slight murmuring which I sounded like "Foolish person". Anyway I proceeded to plead my own case and decided to match their solemnity. And looking straight ahead I raised both my thighs to indicate to them that I was wholly man. Sound in wind and limb. I then forthrightly told them how long I had been the recipient of their twenty per cent award for my disability. Then I emphasized to them that the war had been over for about twenty-seven years. And that I had only been getting my twenty per cent for about three years.

They were circumvented very quickly by one of the board desperate to cut me down to size. "Tell me. Mr..Mr.. What makes you think the War Office should be paying you out money at all? I mean you look pretty fit to me Mr . . ." He was looking down at his notes searching for my name as he spoke. "Yes sir" I replied" I am. I actually walked all the way here from the station as a matter of fact" "Did you indeed?" the pompous one went on with a wry smile at his fellow men on either side. "Well that actually proves my point. Don't you think?"

" No sir," I replied just as spontaneously. "It proves nothing of the sort. It only proves that you're seeing just what you want to see." I stopped for a second then went on. "By the way sir. Can I ask you a personal question?" The somewhat perplexed inquisitor fumbled with his words before nodding assent. "N-not at all" Ask away.." I then asked him "Do you have a family sir?" He nodded. "Yes as a matter of fact I have. I'm a married man with 2 young children," he said proudly. "Good," I said. "And have you ever had the occasion to take them out on a small boat with you?"

For a moment he appeared somewhat flummoxed by my question "Why yes" he stammered. "As a matter of fact I take them out quite often on a lake nearby where I live." I then quickly asked. "And what if one of them happened to fall in the water. Would you have any hesitation in jumping in to rescue any of them?" He shook his head vigorously. "None. I'd be in there like a shot without any hesitation" he said proudly. I jumped in too like a shot "And let me say sir that I would be the first to congratulate you." I said smiling at him "Because its something I certainly couldn't do. Not right away anyway like you." I said bitterly and honestly and sat down abruptly.

There was a noticeable hush amongst the three men sitting opposite me. Then one of the others looked directly at me. "And why do you say that?" he asked. I stood up and answered. "Because to be perfectly honest, I don't know if I would have the guts to do it. Before the war, yes. Like your brave friend there I would have been in there like a shot," I replied somewhat cynically. I then sat down again and folded my arms like I'd seen all the good lawyers do in the movies.

They conferred again. I was asked to leave the room and wait outside. I knew I was taking a chance both in fighting my own case and being so outspoken.

I could lose the lot, and finish up with nothing. But I was determined not to give in. They could stuff their twenty per cent. I thought to myself. I had exaggerated a little, but basically I was speaking the truth. And I was ready to accept the consequences and could only hope that I was being investigated by honourable men. They couldn't all be Colonel Blimps surely. Nor were they in any hurry to give me the benefit of the doubt. I was finally beckoned in to face The Great Ones. "We have listened with great interest to what you had to say Mr McCann. And meantime we are all agreed that you should retain your twenty per cent pension for the time being. Thank you".

I went home reasonably satisfied with my performance. It felt good to let them know that some of us with a mental condition weren't all gibbering idiots. If my message got through that would be something achieved. I would then at least have struck a blow for those other people who didn't have any visual signs of disability but were also often done by very badly. Deep down I knew I had given then something to think about. About a month later I knew for sure that I'd given them something to think about. Because not only did they uphold my disability plea they raised by degree of disability to a whacking 33 per cent. I felt that at last I had been vindicated, and had got some of my own back. What I'd lost on the swings I'd gained on the roundabouts . . .

On reflection and despite the head wound I received which landed me in a mental hospital and almost tempted me into another I have to say that I enjoyed my six years or so in the army. Like I've said before the temptation to go into another asylum for that's what they were called then, was solely to get some recompense from The War Office for something inflicted on me and their miserly determination in denying me a small pension. But ironically enough I regretted nothing. Pleased too in a strange sort of way that I'd managed to scrape through it all with or without distinction.

For when that last electric light goes out in your first Nissen hut and you are told that this is to be your home until you are told otherwise, and your bunk is a palliase stuffed with coarse hair and straw, darkness can be a good bed fellow. For all human frailties surface in the gloom and your thoughts dwell on the morrow and what it may bring .

Last evening's banter and humour if indeed it was ever that, pales into insignificance when you realize that you can count your yesterdays but not your tomorrows. For despite all the chatter and bonhommie that pervaded and once all the niceties are stripped away, this is War and you are being broken in for it. Your only solace may be that occupied bed next to yours and the bed below you. Only then do you appreciate that you are not alone. And those are the thoughts you must cling to

if you're to get through the doom and gloom of those war-ridden times.
The war pensions people don't keep in contact with me now. Somehow I think they've got tired of hauling me up in front of them. Or maybe they're still afraid I might just tell them a few more home-truths again.

Or it may well be that they confine themselves to scouring the obituary columns of the newspapers instead hoping to see my name leap out at them and give the real meaning to that then often used phrase of theirs , "Moribound Account." . . .

Deep down I know they would still love to phone me to see if indeed I am still alive. And I get the impression if the answer was "yes" they would just stop short of saying. "Why?" Those war pensions people may well stick to their policy of payments not being retrospective, payable only from date of application. And nothing for the pain and anguish suffered by persons during the interim period. And I don't suppose for one moment that the system will ever change.

But despite them I still reckon I was paid in full. A payment back-dated too in the fullest sense of the word. In other words, for me it was a case of "Mission Accomplished". For I managed to get that V.I.P. bride of mine out of Nazi Germany after all. And she has been my wife for the past fifty two years. So in retrospect, and as far as I'm concerned she was worth every penny . . . !

**END**

*Edward McCann* M.M.